MONUMENT EDITION

HONEST
JOHN
VANE

J. W. De FOREST

with an introduction by JOSEPH JAY RUBIN

Upsala College
Library
East Orange, N. J.

813.4
D315 h

Copyright 1960 BALD EAGLE PRESS *State College, Pa.*

Printed in the United States of America

L. C. Catalog Card Number 60-5478

Designed by Eleanore Rubin

94811

☞ *PREFACE*

With eleven novels published, J. W. De Forest in 1884 began to negotiate for the printing of a uniform edition. First refusal came from Harper and Brothers, the publishers of *Miss Ravenel's Conversion, Playing The Mischief,* and *Justine's Lovers,* as well as an early travel memoir. Nor could De Forest meet the Harper counter proposal that he buy the plates at half cost and 3,211 inventory copies at cost. On 2 May 1887, after a long stay in Europe, he tried again:

> Can you not make me an offer which I can afford. . . . The form [double columns] of *Playing The Mischief* is now out of fashion. The plates of *Miss Ravenel* are almost the worst that I ever saw; a hundred or a hundred and fifty gross typographical errors. . . . If a library edition is to be got out, I must make the plates at my own expense. . . . Moreover, I must spend months in retouching the works in order to secure a renewal of copyright and to remove some errors in style or matter. At the best I do not hope to sell more than will barely cover the cost of the plates.
>
> My only object is to leave a small monument for myself. And I must hurry.

He had better luck with the holder of two other titles and bought for fifty dollars the plates of *Kate Beaumont* and *Overland.* Those of a third, *The Wetherel Affair,* had been melted accidentally; the abashed publisher transferred publication rights freely to the author.

William Dean Howells had virtually made a second career out of helping and praising De Forest. As far back as 1872 he was insisting that "we are not so much lacking in an American novelist as in a public to recognize him." Now Howells tried in vain to get Ticknor to stereotype the still-neglected work. On 2 September 1887, he wrote a typical note to De Forest:

> I've talked with a good many people about you, and wherever I've met a sound, well-read man, he had read and liked you. . . . I may be mistaken in thinking your books in a uniform edition would succeed now; but I do believe the public has been growing towards your work. The novelist is less woman-rid than he once was, and your masculine tone would be better liked; certainly there is a better chance now for your realism. Good Lord! When one thinks of Stevenson and Haggard selling their tens of thousands and you lacking a publisher, it is hard to be patient.

Three years later in a renewed effort to achieve the edition Howells turned to the owner of a popular "Library" series, J. W. Lovell, whom he described as "a reformed pirate, but so is the best of the rest, and he is trying to publish good books." But neither Lovell nor the despairing novelist responded with enthusiasm. De Forest told Howells on 17 June 1890:

> At present I have an idea that no publisher can put me out successfully until we have got at least a little bit of international copyright. . . . Is Lovell safe? I wonder. I have had three bankrupt publishers, and one who suspended, and have become suspicious.

Howells' final mention of the uniform edition came in

1895, this time a suggestion that De Forest try the house whose imprint would soon go on *The Red Badge of Courage*: Appleton who "have now a most enlightened man in charge of their enterprises — Ripley Hitchcock. The publishers ought to ask you, but I am afraid you will have to ask them." Rather than risk further rebuff, the author of *Honest John Vane,* now in his seventieth year, abandoned his plan to leave a small monument. Longmans in 1898 did the last fiction, *A Lover's Revolt*; a New Haven printer his two volumes of poetry in 1901 and 1902. But when De Forest died in 1906 he had never known the satisfaction of seeing his novels gathered in the format they deserved.

☞ *INTRODUCTION*

In a letter written in January 1876, James Russell Lowell told of his shame the past years when news from America had reached him in Europe:

> Wherever I went I was put on the defensive. Whatever extracts I saw from American papers told of some new fraud or defalcation, public or private. . . . It was fruitless to say that the people were still sound when the Body Politic which draws its life from them showed such blotches and sores. I came home, and instead of wrath at such abominations, I found banter. . . . What fills me with doubt and dismay is the degradation of the moral tone.

Of all the blotches on the Body Politic, the largest and the ugliest was the Credit Mobilier. Examination by press and two Congressional committees proved it infected more legislators than the Erie speculators, the Tweed Ring, Conkling's Custom House, the sale of cadetships, or any other of the many scandals that filled the years after the Civil War. At least eight Congressmen, including the Speaker of the House, three Senators, and the Vice President of the United States were scarred by exposure to what reporters called "the strategy of the subsidy adventurers," the lobbyists of the Credit Mobilier. When the Wilson Committee tried in 1873 to probe the extent of financial manipulation, its investigators found that "the books have been kept in such a way, and the transactions have been of such a character, as that their true nature has been very much disguised." Cost estimates of engineers had vanished; General Grenville M. Dodge refused to come to Washington to testify. Skilled counsel, including the egregious Ben Butler, repudiated every charge, clouded every fact except the basic one — that greedy men had broken the law. The Wilson Committee concluded that the three Credit Mobilier contracts for $93,546,287.28 brought a profit of $43,925,328.34. No wonder that an expense account for $18,000 at Willard's Hotel seemed a trifle.

In June 1862, Congress had responded with the Pacific Railway Act to long-demonstrated need for a continental military and commercial link. In 1864, prodded by Union Pacific lobbyists, Congress increased the bounty to the road builders. It was now that directors of the Union Pacific operating not as trustees of a potential national treasure but as private promoters began to exploit the huge acreage and government currency bonds provided by generous legislation. The device to be used, the assigning to themselves of road-construction contracts, was neither legal nor novel, but it had proved itself profitable in other parts of the country, especially the West. The risk in this wilful disregard of law lay in the fact that those who assumed the contracts would be personally liable for all debts. "They therefore took steps to procure corporate powers as a shield against such risk, and secured for that purpose the control of a corporation known as the Credit Mobilier." In March 1864, the Vice President of the Union Pacific bought the charter of the obscure Pennsylvania Agency which had been "snaked through the Legislature" with virtually unlimited powers to build railways in the South and the West; it was renamed prophetically after the scandal-soiled, French joint-stock venture by one of the lobbyists with European experience, the notorious George Francis Train. "The Fiscal Agency," wrote a contemporary observer, "was a chimera; the Credit Mobilier entered the skin of it as devils possessed the crazy man." Liability would now be limited to the amount of subscription to stock.

Within the year the Credit Mobilier, now a "corporation inside of the original corporation," contracted to build track west from Omaha for its alias. At a cost to the Union Pacific of $12,974,416.24, the Credit Mobilier realized a profit of $5,168,233.91. It was over the execution of this first contract that the chief engineer of the Union Pacific, Peter A. Day, resigned. He refused to lend his name to estimates rigged higher than experience warranted; he objected to orders from directors to increase costs by building unneeded heavy embankments. His resignation "from the best position in my profession this country has ever offered to any man" was accepted and General Dodge replaced him. Mrs. Dodge soon owned one hundred shares of Credit Mobilier stock.

Parts of the second contract displayed further bizarre concepts of trusteeship. According to the Wilson Committee, the Credit Mobilier charged $1,104,000 for fifty-eight miles of track already built and accepted under the first contract. But the terms of the third contract, the "wildest . . . made by a civilized man" surpassed the first two in audacity and magnitude of profit — "if that is the proper word to be used in this connection." It would be identified as the creature of Oakes Ames, manufacturer of shovels and plows, since 1862 a Republican member of Congress from Massachusetts, and since a corporate election of October 1866, in power with his brother among the Credit Mobilier directors. On 16

August 1867, Ames contracted with the Union Pacific to build 667 miles of track for $47,000,000. Earnings were to be split among the stockholders of the Credit Mobilier, thereby guaranteeing profits for both parties, for "all large stockholders in the Union Pacific were also stockholders in the Credit Mobilier." Congressional inquiry also proved that Ames charged the Union Pacific from $42,000 to $96,000 per mile, and that "this contract extended over 138 miles of road already completed and accepted." The 138 miles had cost only $27,000 per mile originally! As a result of receiving pay for work done by others, the Credit Mobilier declared swift dividends; on 12 December 1867, the operators divided "among themselves as profits at that date, a larger sum than they ever put at risk in the whole transaction."

Though the stock of the Credit Mobilier, as Ames' counsel argued, was not on the market at this time and had "no ascertained price," all owners reasonably understood that the $47,000,000 contract had increased its value. "Profits are reported to have been enormous, — reported only," wrote Charles Francis Adams, Jr., a careful investigator of speculation in 1869, for "throughout all this there is nothing but hearsay and street rumor to rely upon." Dividends, according to one of the rumors, reached eleven hundred per cent; *The Nation* guessed fifteen hundred per cent.

Contract and capital secured, Ames, who had become interested in the Union Pacific while a member of the Committee on Railroads in the House, now turned his promotional energy to Washington. His mission was twofold: the prevention of restrictive legislation to regulate transportation rates, for Ames and his group, unlike some of the other promoters, believed in the commercial future of the Union Pacific; but above all Ames wanted to safeguard construction profits. With the opening of the winter session of Congress in December 1867, according to the official record of his peers, he "entered into contracts with a considerable number of members of Congress, both Senators and Representatives, to let them have shares of stock in the Credit Mobilier Company, at par, with interest thereon from the first day of the previous July. It does not appear that in any instance he asked any of these persons to pay a higher price than the value and interest, nor that Mr. Ames used any special effort or urgency to get these persons to take it."

To judge by the number of Congressional takers Ames entered in his memorandum book, none needed special pleading. The pre-contract price of the stock was recognized for the bargain it was, with a soaring value too tempting to reject. (Washington gossip in January 1868, had it that the stock "to anyone else but a friend of Mr. Ames" was worth four times its par value.) And Ames was a considerate broker: he guaranteed at least ten per cent profit; he even advanced the total purchase price of the stock. It proved all too easy for a fellow-legislator after 16 August to buy at July's deflated rates, pay for the stock from the profits accrued after 16 August and held in reserve by Ames, and quickly realize new dividends — without risking a cent of his own limited ($5,000) Congressional salary. The frank reason Ames gave for using this method to safeguard the Credit Mobilier from government scrutiny resounded through Washington and the country: "There is no difficulty in getting men to look after their own property."

"Hoax" Ames, as the New York *Herald* named him, was not the only lobbyist working to protect railroad interests and profits, nor was there accord among the several groups; in fact, quarrels and incriminations sped their exposure. The one-time head of the Credit Mobilier, Thomas C. Durant, now hostile to the Ames group, was an old hand at influencing legislators: as Vice President of the Union Pacific he had exhausted a "suspense account" of $435,754.21 in winning the Railroad Act of 1864. A third member, Henry S. McComb of Delaware, claimed in anger that he could not take care of his friends because Ames had secured all available stock. When McComb sued to recover 343 shares worth, in his estimate $300,000, the feud with Ames became public knowledge. Demands for official exposure of the entire Credit Mobilier followed McComb's detailed affidavits which charged Ames with using the stock to corrupt Congress.

There had been early airings of suspicion. Disillusioned like his brothers and Walt Whitman by unchecked rapacity, Charles Francis Adams made the "legerdemain of paper financiering" his target in the January 1869, *North American Review:*

> Who, then, constitute the Credit Mobilier? It is but another name for the Pacific Railroad Ring. The members of it are in Congress; they are trustees for the bondholders, they are directors, they are stockholders, they are contractors; in Congress they vote the subsidies, in New York they receive them, on the plains they spend them, and in the Credit Mobilier they divide them. . . . As stockholders they own the road, as mortgagees they have a lien upon it, as directors they contract for its construction, and as members of the Credit Mobilier they build it.

Adams, like Andrew Johnson before him, saw the consequences of this "thimble-rig" operation:

> Here . . . is every vicious element of railroad construction and management; here is costly construction, entailing future taxation on trade; here are tens of millions of fictitious capital; here is a road built

on the sale of its bonds, and with the aid of subsidies; here is every element of cost recklessly exaggerated, and the whole at some future day is to make itself felt as a burden on the trade which it is to create, and will surely hereafter constitute a source of corruption in the politics of the land, and a resistless power in its legislature.

In April of that year, a month before Leland Stanford drove the last spike of gold into the last tie of laurel joining the Union Pacific and the Central Pacific at Promontory Point, Congress heard the first charges of fraud. In his devious way Jim Fisk, the Erie "raider," also staged an assault on the Credit Mobilier which brought further notoriety. But it was the presidential campaign of 1872 that made investigation inevitable. From the Liberal Republicans — a public response to the corruption of the Grant regime — the nation learned during a "war of mud and missiles" of specific accusations. With the Liberal Republicans led by newspaper editors as responsible as Bryant, Whitelaw Reid, Henry Watterson, and Horace White, and with the Democrats eager for issues, the scandal could not be suppressed. In the midst of the campaign, Dana's *Sun* documented charges that the Credit Mobilier had bought its way into Congress by reprinting Ames' letters to McComb with names of Congressmen and numbers of their shares. When the Forty-Second Congress met in December 1872, the House urged by Speaker James G. Blaine, one of the alleged buyers of stock, moved to investigate whether any member "was bribed by Oakes Ames, or any other person or corporation, in any matter touching his legislative duty." A committee, named after its chairman, Judge Luke Poland of Vermont, a respected, white-haired, white-whiskered "kind and generous gentleman," started to take testimony 12 December; it sat until 19 February 1873. Those who believed in portents noted that the committee room was at the foot of a long flight of dark stairs.

Deliberating over hundreds of pages of testimony, Judge Poland detected "painfully conflicting" statements; he found "an entire variance" as to the transaction between Ames and "Pig Iron" Kelley of Pennsylvania. Somehow the committee concluded that Ames was "guilty of selling to members of Congress shares of stock in the Credit Mobilier of America, for prices much below the true value of such stock, with intent thereby to influence the votes and decisions of such members in matters to be brought before Congress. *Resolved,* That Mr. Oakes Ames be, and he is hereby, expelled from his seat as a member of this House." James Brooks of New York, the leader of the Democrats in the House, was also expelled; he had violated law in using his position as government director of the Union Pacific to procure stock.

Congress changed its verdict to reprimand, but Ames and Brooks found little comfort in the lesser disgrace for both died within the year. None of the others received official punishment of any kind; neither the members who admitted purchase of shares but pleaded ignorance of the implications of large, quick profits on little or no initial investment — like the chairman of that powerful fiscal agency, the Ways and Means Committee — nor those who like Vice President Colfax embarrassed investigators and country by awkward denial and fantastic explanation. A Senate committee recommended the expulsion of James W. Patterson, but no action resulted; five days later the term of the New Hampshire senator expired.

The press shared Ames' anger that he was offered up as the "prime sacrifice to appease a public clamor or expiate the sins of others." The gist of editorial comment upon the Poland Report was that the briber had been punished but not the bribe takers and that the investigation was

> a miserable effort to hunt up a couple of scape goats to bear the sins of those who were to be saved from expulsion. The people of the United States feel deeply the shame and humiliation of the whole affair, and they, let us thank Heaven, have not learned to consider party claims when the national honor is at stake. They had a right to expect of the Committee either a clear vindication of the accused parties, or an impartial rigid meting out of justice to them. The result is appearing. They see their trusted public servants convicted of falsehood, stained with the ownership of the most questionable property of the present day, and they are gravely asked by a Committee of Congress to believe that the men whom they have trusted and honored, and whom they know to be keen, shrewd, practical business men, are a parcel of ignorant fools, unable to manage a simple investment in stocks with the prudence or care of the most ordinary man of business.

Gath of the Chicago *Tribune* went so far as to publish his belief that Congress was "diseased and corrupt . . . and has wholly lost its own self-respect and the confidence of the country."

The Wilson Committee appointed to examine the relationship between the Union Pacific and the Credit Mobilier partially redeemed the reputation of the House. Its report was devastating in its analysis of the interlocking corporations, its tone harsher and more indignant than Judge Poland's, its conclusion, echoing Adams' earlier blast, a refutation of the "patriot" defense attempted by some of the stockholders:

> It is also said that it is unjust to look at this question in the light of the present; that we should go

back to the condition of things before the road was built, when the whole scheme seemed, to the prudent capitalists of the country, visionary and perilous. This is true; and if these gentlemen assumed great risk from which others shrank, and thereby great benefits inured to the public, they should have all due credit. But we think they differed from other capitalists, not in taking a risk, but in having discovered that the road could be built at vast profit without risk, the resources furnished by the Government being more than ample for the purpose.

The recommendation of the Wilson Committee that the Attorney General sue the Union Pacific to recover fraudulent profits never resulted in the recovery of a penny.

Some of the Congressmen who had been hurt by the Credit Mobilier but not officially disgraced remained in Washington. Some, like the fictitious Honest John Vane, were reëlected. (But those who knew called him Weathercock Vane.) One even became President of the United States. Not too many years later the stockholders of the Union Pacific erected a monument to Oakes Ames and his brother on the highest ground touched by the road they helped build. J. W. De Forest had already done his bit to keep fresh the memory of the Credit Mobilier.

II

On the first page of his Civil War novel, *Miss Ravenel's Conversion*, De Forest gave his concept of history: "An obscure American author remarks in one of his rejected articles . . . that every great historical event reverberates through the fortunes of private and even secluded individuals." Only months after the Poland and Wilson findings, *The Atlantic Monthly* for July 1873 carried the first of five consecutive installments telling of the reverberations of the Credit Mobilier upon De Forest's narrative consciousness. His fictitious lobbyist, Darius Dorman, had predicted a "one-legged report" from Congress; *Honest John Vane* is the novelist's try at a truer version of what he called the Juggernaut of swindling.

By 1873, he could draw upon experience rich enough to handle this national subject. Now forty-seven, his first book, the 500-page *History of the Indians of Connecticut*, had appeared twenty-two years earlier and identified a career-long interest. Its epigraph from Lamentations, "Our inheritance is turned to strangers, our houses to aliens," showed his temper; and its contents, sanctioned by the Connecticut Historical Society, his capacity for sustained, accurate research at the Yale Library, Hartford archives, and the Massachusetts Historical Society. He did not hesitate to challenge the worth of some of the manuscripts in the collection of President Stiles for "depending too much on the reminiscences of aged men and women, unaccustomed to making statements for publication, and within whose recollections the slender numbers of the Indians multiplied as wonderfully as the two buckram men of Falstaff." His first novel, *Witching Times*, serialized in *Putnam's* in 1856 and 1857, used Puritan Salem, the setting for one of his short stories and a ballad; his last novel, *A Lover's Revolt* (1898), would recreate colonial Boston and the first battles for independence. Nor was his historical interest provincial, for with this mining of American backgrounds he printed several papers on the history of the Papacy; his *Atlantic* essay on "The Cradle of the Human Race" (February 1878) received favorable notice in Europe. (In 1890 he and Howells exchanged letters over the value of this early study.) In addition to finding material in the Revolution, the Civil War, and Apache skirmishes (*Overland*, 1871),

Upsala College
Library
East Orange, N. J.

he wrote a learned, exciting critique of "Caesar's Art of War and of Writing" (*Atlantic*, September 1879). De Forest is one of our first professional military historians.

He was born in Humphreysville, Connecticut, 31 March 1826, into a family proud of its descent from the de Forests of Avesnes; he would use the Huguenot strain in *Kate Beaumont* (1872) and *The Bloody Chasm* (1881). Too frail after typhoid to study at nearby Yale in "that city of geometry and Puritanism," this orphaned son of a textile manufacturer travelled like Melville and Twain to the Near East. His *Oriental Acquaintance; or, Letters from Syria* (1856), is a young man's record of the journey from Boston to Smyrna, Jerusalem, and Lebanon. A reviewer found qualities that are evident in later writings: brilliance without bombast, liveliness without extravagance, and a "tone of thoughtful criticism." (On the cover the publishers, Dix, Edwards, announced "Herman Melville's New Book, *The Piazza Tales*" and Frederick L. Olmsted's *Journey in the Seaboard Slave States*.) In 1879, when De Forest was "frozen by neglect" and certain that "our novel-reading public is mainly a female or a very juvenile public, and wants something nearer its own mark of intellect and taste, as for instance, 'Helen's Babies' and 'That Husband of Mine,'" he rewrote this tour into *Irene The Missionary*, a tale of American love in Beirut and Damascus. It was his sardonic hope that the large public interested in missionaries would believe that the author was "either a returned missionary, or a lady."

Like Hawthorne, Howells, and Henry James, he lived in Europe. "Pursued by the fretting enmity of a monotonous invalidism," he shipped to Florence where he met Horatio Greenough — whose sculpture John Vane passed every day in Washington. Then, after Venice, the water cure under Priessnitz at Graefenburg. Two months of incessant hydropathy and chilling aeration improved his health, and he moved to Paris where he learned to speak French while arguing politics, and developed an enduring enthusiasm for French writers: in turn he praised Sand, Stendhal, Balzac, Hugo, Taine, Zola. Then, back to beloved Florence and a life of "supreme laziness." There were "whole weeks during which . . . I scarcely ever did anything more violent than pull on . . . boots or smoke a hard-drawing cigar." He admired the Campanile, the Church of Santa Croce, Bologna's *Mercury,* Michelangelo's *David,* and found even more "sensuousness of enjoyment" in the Arno at night, the hills, the groves of the Cascine — wonders of the wonder-filled city James and Howells also noted. Always sensitive to the nuance of language — he would record Selnarten Bowen's "low-downer" talk, John Vane's aberrations, and Abner Sly's Yankee dialect in *A Lover's Revolt* — he admired the speech of a girl named Maria from Siena, "where the language is the purest." One of his friends read Bulwer, but De Forest spent his hours trying to turn Hawthorne's *The House of the Seven Gables* into Tuscan, for a Florentine editor had agreed to publish the translation in the feuilleton of his weekly journal. But the

> choice epithets and metaphysical ideas of the Pyncheon family's history stumbled us to such a degree that we would only make out about three pages a day; and after finishing three chapters and part of a fourth, the work fell through in consequence of my departure from Florence. In fact it was a little beyond our capacities, for I was by no means a master in the graces of Italian composition.

Other legacies of his Italian stay were a thorough knowledge of Dante, high regard for Manzoni's *I Pro-*

messi Sposi, Guido's *Beatrice de Cenci,* Carlo Dolci — "in spite of Ruskin" — and memory of a moment like this described in *Seacliff* (1859):

> When I was in Naples, standing in one of the halls of gigantic Museo Borbonico, I saw an English girl of about eighteen, staid, quaint, and Jane Eyreish in aspect, step up to an antique copy of that beautiful boy-bust known as the Young Augustus; kiss its forehead, and then walk quietly away without glancing around her to see whether or not that strange action had been noticed by the loiterers whose footsteps echoed down the long galleries.

Years later in a comment to Howells (1879) he gave a mature reaction to an unrecorded phase of his continental experience:

> What a society that is in Venice and Florence! You are . . . right in showing up the American lady who gets on her knees to it. It is quite time we should protest against the flunkeyism of the *colonie de Paris.*

But he waited too long before turning into fiction his *European Acquaintance: Being Sketches of People in Europe* (1858). *The Bloody Chasm* (1881) with its Parisian setting, coming after his reading of *Daisy Miller* and its *succês de haîne,* as he phrased it, is his weakest novel.

Home again, he married a girl met at the New Haven House where he was living — like Colburne in *Miss Ravenel's Conversion.* Harriet Shephard's father was a versatile scientist with an international reputation as a mineralogist and authority on meteorites. An early associate of Benjamin Silliman at Yale and a contributor to the *American Journal of Science and Arts,* since 1834 he had been Professor of Chemistry at Charleston (South Carolina) Medical College, and since 1845 also Professor of Natural History at Amherst. The De Forests accompanied Dr. Shephard to Charleston where the novelist began to observe the "tableau" of society in depth that he recreated later in one of his major novels, *Kate Beaumont* (1872). But onrushing sectional hostility ended the Southern stay in 1861 when the three made the last boat north. De Forest's "Charleston Under Arms" in *The Atlantic* that April is a valuable report of the South Carolina mood just before the assault on Sumter, as well as a reflection of the author's political sympathy: Buchanan is a "well-intentioned imbecile" who loves the "chaotic *status quo*"; the South Carolineans "see but one side of the shield, — which is quite different as we know, from the custom of the rest of mankind."

De Forest memorialized his father-in-law as the tender, unworldly Dr. Ravenel; and he used the scientist's knowledge in *Overland*, where the many pages of remarkable description of the Southwest owe much of their technical authenticity to Dr. Shephard and his library. Thurstane, the officer-hero of this "rattling good yarn," as Brander Matthews called it, craves "leisure for the study of geology, mineralogy, and chemistry"; Frank McAlister of *Kate Beaumont* has studied earth sciences in Germany and seeks an American professorship; De Vries of *Irene The Missionary* is an ethnologist whose research on the origins of the Philistines is ended by the Civil War.

III

De Forest's reading all these years had the range of a man who followed his own high intelligence rather than channels marked by academic hands. He sought knowledge in ancient history, political science, economics, and religion. Within two pages of *Honest John Vane* he mentions Niebuhr, Arnold, Grote, Curtius, Mommsen,

Adam Smith, Mill, Bastiat, and Henry C. Carey. One of
his short story characters reads Bishop Colenso, the con-
troversial exegete of Genesis and Saint Paul. Irene Grant,
the would-be missionary, has spent most of her young
life in her father's library "poring over" Plutarch, Rollin,
and the *Classical Dictionary*. *Overland* found space for
Darwin and Spencer; *Playing The Mischief* (1875) contains an extended and memorable debate on evolution,
with Colonel Murray (one of his finest creations) speaking for De Forest when he announces, "What with Max
Muller and Whitney, and Dalton and Lecky, and Spencer
and Darwin, and forty more amazing chaps, I am up to
my eyes in new ideas all the while." Galileo, Kepler,
Newton, and Laplace prove to be among the "amazing
chaps" Colonel Murray knows. An elder lawyer in *Justine's Lovers* (1878) asks, "Have you read Galton's 'Her-
editary Descent of Genius'? No? You should read it.
It is a great and terrible revelation. We are the sons of
our fathers, and not of our little resolves." The young
British officer in *A Lover's Revolt*, worried after the turn
of the first day's fighting at Lexington and Concord,
wants the War Office to send a new general. "If we were
only on good terms with Sparta, and could borrow
Xantippus, Gylippus, or Brasidas!" *A Lover's Revolt* is
in itself proof of De Forest's study of American and British history.

Ruled early, as he confessed, by the "craze in his head
that he will some day write a great novel," he read wide-
ly in fiction, inevitably cataloguing for possible use those
authors who won his admiration, rejecting the many others. Irving he honored for the creation of Ichabod Crane
and the longer *History of New York* — in *Seacliff* he
toasted the memory of Wouter Van Twiller — but recognized limitations in scope. Cooper aroused as little en-

thusiasm in De Forest as in Twain. Paulding, Brown, Kennedy, Simms did nothing for him: "they wrote about ghosts, and the ghosts have vanished utterly." He found Hawthorne's *Scarlet Letter, Blithedale Romance,* and *The House of the Seven Gables* "full of acute spiritual analysis, of the light of the other worlds," but in recoiling from complete approval of an artist for whom he had profound reverence, De Forest revealed that his own theory of fiction urged other directions. Hawthorne's novels were

> characterized by only a vague consciousness of this life, and by graspings that catch little but the subjective of humanity. . . . Such personages as Hawthorne creates belong to the wide realm of art rather than to our nationality. . . . They are what Yankees might come to be who shut themselves up for life to meditate in old manses. They have no sympathy with this eager and laborious people, which takes so many newspapers, builds so many railroads, does the most business on a given capital, wages the biggest war in proportion to its population, believes in the physically impossible and does some of it. Hawthorne's characters cannot talk? Certainly not in the style of this western world; rather in the language of men who never expressed themselves but on paper, in dreams.

More than a decade later Henry James also found that Hawthorne "was not in the least a realist — he was not to my mind enough of one."

But De Forest paid Hawthorne the honor of going to Salem six years after *The Scarlet Letter* for the setting of his first novel. And *Witching Times,* built upon the Puritan documents read at the Massachusetts Historical Society, is an impressive beginning, with its powerful figure of Henry More struggling to hold back what he calls the witchcraft avalanche. If More is, in his creator's concept, a New England Quixote who reads his remote kinsman's *Utopia* and goes to an undeserved death uncowed by obsessed magistrates, his daughter Rachel is Hester's younger, virginal sister. The tragic Giles Cory, Justice John Hawthorne, and Cotton Mather — whom the author excoriates — all have their place in *Witching Times*. Unlike his other novels first serialized in magazines, *Witching Times* was never reprinted in book form.

The native work that came close to his ideal concept was *Uncle Tom's Cabin*. De Forest recognized faults in plot, in a little girl unlike any other little girl, in the "village twaddle," in an "impeccable Uncle Tom" (see *his* handling of Uncle Tom in *Miss Ravenel, Kate Beaumont*, and some of the short fiction). But he had known Northerners like those in the book, "and we have seen such Southerners, no matter what the people south of Mason and Dixon's line may protest." Its strength lay in the "picture of American life, drawn with a few strong and passionate strokes, not filled in thoroughly, but still a portrait." No other native novel — by 1868 when he made these judgments — painted "American life so broadly, truly and sympathetically"; or offered material comparable to a *Newcomes*, a *Vanity Fair*, a *Miserables*, *Little Dorrit*, or Trollope's *Small House at Allington*. Somehow he missed *Moby-Dick*. Later (1879) he would say to Howells, "There is James . . . who belongs to our school, and who yet seems to be forging ahead." But by 1887 he wrote him:

> I am glad to have found Tolstoi. I had been reduced, in the matter of novels, to Zola and you; and two men can't write fast enough for one reader. There are other good story writers, such as James, Cable, Craddock. But they are not to me satisfactory

and instructing novelists. I now want somebody from whom I can learn the *what* and the *how*. Isn't it odd the creator of Daisy Miller fails somewhat in larger painting of human nature?

He warmed to a younger American girl who picked daisies and violets at the Cascine, Effie Bowen of that Florentine evocation, *Indian Summer.*

In almost all of his fiction De Forest is the conscious humorist. In *Honest John Vane* he sustains the wit that begins with the first paragraph. He perpetuates lines like "the main work of Congress is done out of sight, like that of a mole," and the description of Olympia Vane as a "veteran flirt, trained to tough coquetry in many a desperate skirmish." Of a 93-year-old character in "The Lauson Tragedy," he wrote "You might travel over him for a week without discovering half his wonders"; Father Higgins, a priest who converts cannibals, finds that to be "worshipped is infinitely more agreeable than being eaten." In *Playing The Mischief,* his humorous masterpiece, he gives us Hollowbread's "popcorn" way of costuming himself and the affairs of the "bloomer girl," Squire Nancy Appleyard. In *A Lover's Revolt,* the Yankee rustic, Abner Sly, and his "pudgy" horse. Admittedly he knew Dickens — and Joe Miller — as well as his comic countrymen: he cites the "impudent" letters of Jack Downing, the "hyperbolical" Mr. John Phoenix, the "cacographic quips" of Josh Billings' *Allminax,* the "impudent whimsies" of Artemus Ward, Holmes, and the "droll" exaggerations of *Roughing It* by that other commentator upon corruption in Washington — though Howells in 1887 wished that De Forest would understand and like Twain "better than you do."

His two humorless novels, *Justine's Lovers* and *The Bloody Chasm,* came after the death of his wife and the onset of prolonged illness, a time of despair and subdued creativity that he tried to rally from by seeking a change of scene. He asked Howells to secure for him a diplomatic post from President Hayes, but no embassy or consulate opened its doors to the writer who had used Republican political folly as a target. Like the invalid, impoverished Justine whose way of life fate also changed, he could not read his favorite novels — let alone write with early strength and wit. This is De Forest in 1878:

> The Bible was the one and only book which could occupy me. I wandered through it, and secludedly dwelt in it, for hours every day. It had become a novelty, very wonderful and entrancing. In old and well-known passages I found marvels which I had never noted before. . . . There was no profound or peculiar religious experience connected with this incessant study. . . . It was much as if I had met, for the first time in many years, some beloved guardian of my childhood, still as tender and as trusted as ever. . . . For the profoundly stricken, for the stricken who cannot lift their hands to struggle, it is a home of healing and refuge, compared with which all other asylums are bleak deserts, windblown and haunted by simoons.

Out of this "perpetual haunting of the Holy Land of the Scriptures" came a rediscovery of Lamentations and the Psalms.

Taste and temperament always took De Forest beyond national boundaries. In the preface to *The Downing Legends* (1901), he cautioned that the poems were extravaganzas, and that they "will not be liked except by readers who like such works as the Odyssey, the Arabian Nights, the Orlando Innamorato of Boiardo and Berni, the Orlando Furioso of Ariosto, the Pilgrim's Progress, Gulliver's Travels, Knickerbocker's History of New York and Hawthorne's Wonder Tales." In "The City of Brass" he eulogizes the author of *The Arabian Nights*, that "fervid genius to whom we must bow as to one of the unknown gods of literature"; the tales are the favorite readings of Bentley Armitage in *Kate Beaumont*. In *Miss Ravenel's Conversion* he quotes from Cervantes and Balzac, and likens Colonel Carter, his hard-drinking, promiscuous professional soldier who is one of the powerful creations of nineteenth-century American fiction, to Scott's Dugald Dalgetty. A perceptive reviewer called his Mrs. Larue "a Becky Sharpe with more grace and tenderness." The literary young hero of *Seacliff* remembers the title-page of *Pendennis* and Irish novels; the scientist in *Kate Beaumont* recites Schiller, and De Vries of *Irene The Missionary*, Persian poetry. In several passages De Forest shows his intimacy with Sam Weller and that other eminent Dickensian, Jefferson Brick of *Martin Chuzzlewit*. In *Playing The Mischief* he speaks of Trollope; one character in *The Wetherel Affair* (1873) says, "Cousin John, you run over with Emerson as I do with Tupper." His epithet for Senator Ironman is Dundreary, from the E. H. Sothern role in *Our American Cousin*, the play that attracted not only the novelist but, unfortunately, President Lincoln. Detailed to duty after the Civil War in Greenville, South Carolina, he found the place and time to read Gibbon, Hume, Goldsmith, Addison. He questioned American neglect of an Italian favorite; the reason he offered to Howells in 1887 may well explain American neglect of De Forest:

> I cannot understand any more than you why *I Promessi Sposi* is not held in general enthusiastic reverence. Perhaps it is because the novel-reading public is in the main a young or feminine public, and naturally prefers a work of a lower grade than

Manzoni could do. Do you think our novel-reading public cares much for Hamlet, or Don Quixote, or any masterpiece . . . it appears to me that the ordinary or uncultivated mind revolts from anything much higher than itself. Here is another lofty stair to climb; here is a new dialect of thought and even of language to struggle with; here is somebody insulting us by speaking a foreign language.

Turgenev also linked *Hamlet* and *Don Quixote.*

In each of his twelve novels and in his short fiction, De Forest at times used his reading, his erudition, rather than his invention to define character or to create mood, tone, texture. In *Witching Times* the Salem landscape in March is compared to the trees in the *Inferno;* the frightful whispers of evil are those Christian heard in the *Pilgrim's Progress,* the book he loved for its pure diction as well as its parable. In *Overland* he turned to Prescott and Shenstone's pastorals; to create awe and horror he loaded a dozen pages with afreets from *The Arabian Nights,* Dore's illustrations, *Vathek,* Milton's hell, with Bunyan's Dark Valley "the two sublimest landscapes . . . ever presented to the imagination." Thurstone on a waterless trek pursued by Apaches is like Christian "listening to the screams and curses of devils." The desperate Justine, fallen "from the paradise of brown-stone fronts and Aubusson carpets," waiting for an interview with the Secretary who might offer her a Washington clerkship, thinks of Tennyson's "Sleeping Palace" and of Muller's *Calling of the Condemned to Execution.* When Justine leaves without the job, a friend consoles her, "I saw you descending those bitter stairs — the stairways that Dante cursed — the stairways of the great." The classical mood at the beginning of *Irene The Missionary* is evoked by a scholar who apostrophizes "Those Greeks,

those marvellous Greeks" and tells the *Iliad* episode of
Zeus and the body of his son, Sarpedon. The romance
in *Irene* almost ends because of conflict between the
"student of the Scriptures" and the student of Balzac.
Poe's "To Annie" closes two deathbed scenes as moving
as those in Dickens or an American favorite, Stowe's *The
Pearl of Orr's Island*. Painters as different as Michelangelo, Millais, Greuze, and Fra Angelico ride through
New Mexico; sculpture by Praxiteles and Gerome's nude
Cleopatra ornament *Playing The Mischief;* Kate Beaumont reminds her beloved of Murillo's *Immaculate Vir-
gin.*

Seacliff is even more allusive than *Overland,* for the
narrator, Fitz Hugh, is a writer rather than a soldier and
has at hand Coleridge, Byron, Tennyson, as well as verse
by Alexander Smith, the ubiquitous Bunyan and Cervantes, and "that unparalleled narrative of crime and
criminals, the "Memoirs of Vidocq." (De Forest's sub-
title is "The Mystery of the Westervelts," and he ends
the book with a murder and a suicide.) A work which
in the judgment of Edward Wagenknecht "represents
about as close an approach to the British country-house
novel as can be made in America," *Seacliff* has the additional interest of resembling Gide's *Les Faux-Monna-
yeurs* for it is a novel told by a novelist at work, with
disquisitions on his craft like this by Fitz Hugh:

> Perhaps the embryo Scott is not yet aware that
> true portraiture of character, — just analysis of hu-
> man nature, — is the gem which lends practical
> value to a romance, gives it the power of fact under
> the grace of fiction, and places it among those kingly
> gifts that the world rejoices to receive. . . . The young
> author, no wonder of mind, but still possessed of tal-
> ents, writes away with a good heart at first; but after
> finishing two or three chapters he becomes vaguely

conscious that there is some important element of
immortality wanting to his work; and so, merely to
save it from lethargy and early death, he dashes into
rapid movement, passionate situations, and a rhetoric
flavored with gunpowder. His own stores of these
valuables soon giving out, he plagiarizes in his desperation, stealing one man's hero, another man's murder, and a third man's simile.

We are told in *Playing The Mischief* that Colonel Murray "made one think of a venerable and entirely sane
Don Quixote," and Hollowbread of "poor Sancho Panza."
Josephine Murray, "wise as a serpent" and one of a sister-
hood that includes Mrs. Larue, Olympia Vane, and Mrs.
Chester, impressed by the Parliamentary series, says, "I
have been reading Trollope lately. . . . Mr. Palliser is
so amusing with his labors as Chancellor of the Ex-
chequer! Now, who is your Mr. Palliser in Congress?"
John Vane is "that sham Aristides"; newspapermen as
well as Colonel Carter are Dugald Dalgettys; Sykes
Drummond resents the fact that he shares the name of
a Dickens' murderer; in a moment of stress De Forest
has one of his women remember the speech of a heroine
in Bulwer's *Pelham*. Again and again he turns to Biblical
archetypes of evil — not only Satan but Ananias. And
he summarizes a remarkable scene in *Kate Beaumont*
by writing of the psychotic "social gymnast" who has an
uncontrollable passion for younger men, Mrs. Chester:
"She was a cracked old Cleopatra waiting on a young
rough of an Antony." Though this is one of the least
allusive of De Forest's novels, Frank McAlister worries
over the limitations of American literature, and the author
describes the narrative tensions as those created by the
Montagues and Capulets of South Carolina. One wonders if Twain remembered the feud of the Beaumonts

and the McAlisters when he came to his Shepherdsons and Grangerfords.

Even lesser works like *The Wetherel Affair, Justine's Lovers,* and *The Bloody Chasm* are rich in literary interest, with their turning to Milton, Scott, Cervantes, and Bunyan: *Grace Abounding* is that "eloquent confession of a devout soul, written in simplest, purest, most idiomatic English — a book which great literary ability could not imitate either in feeling or style. . . . It equals Herodotus in childlike grace, and it surpasses him in sublimity and pathos." (Twain, it will be recalled, has Huck Finn tell us that he "read considerable in *Pilgrim's Progress.*" He found the "statements was interesting, but tough." And *Don Quixote* also sparked Tom Sawyer's imagination.) John Bowlder, the transcendental philosopher of *The Wetherel Affair,* worships Emerson, reads Whitman, and, carried away by *Walden,* builds a woodland hermitage. Like De Forest, Bowlder admits that his poetry is inferior to Burns' but rationalizes, "what I have that give I freely, like a bird." Count Poloski, the suspect foreigner in this Wilkie Collins-like murder mystery, claims that he has written a treatise on the "Migrations of Metaphor," and illustrates by calling the English language a tangled forest. Poloski's other favorite conversation piece is "the world-sorrow" in literature:

> We must not laugh at the world-sorrow. . . . You practical Anglo-Saxons delight to laugh at it; you call Byron humbug because he felt it and sang it. But you are wrong. The world-sorrow is a true and beautiful emotion. . . . The illimitable Shakespeare divined and described it. The melancholy of Hamlet comes not altogether from his troubles; it is partly world-sorrow. When we behold that great drama from this one of its many sides, we see that Hamlet was in part a prophecy of Rousseau and Byron.

A third character in *The Wetherel Affair*, Walter Lehming, is a professional journalist who bemoans the poor
taste of editors and readers of weeklies who avoid Dickens, Hawthorne, Trollope, and Charles Reade. He assures a young woman, in a judgment that adheres to
De Forest's own work,

> You may trust Reade. . . . He will always give
> you a well-ordered plot and an interesting sequence
> of incidents. Some of his characters, too, are sketch-
> ed vigorously, and have the broad traits of human
> nature recognizable everywhere.

Lehming's comment on style, made at the time of the
composition of *Honest John Vane*, shows De Forest's approach to rhetoric: the journalist praises the "natural"
figure of a pumpkin pie, for it is "drawn from common
life, like the similes of Socrates and Emerson." Lehming's
analysis of the difficulty met by American writers is as
valuable as his talk of books. In his strong image, native
artists are being ruined by competition from all the ath-
letes of foreign literature — an argument De Forest repeated as the years continued to deprive him of reputation.

Justine's only talent is the writing of hymns. Encouraged by one of her "lovers" to follow Watts and Keble,
she turns Biblical stories into ballads, "wondering inno-
cently the while that Macaulay should not have written
them" rather than the "Lays of Ancient Rome." Virginia
Beaufort in *The Bloody Chasm*, which the war dug between North and the remnants of the South, moves from
ruined Charleston to Paris, "that city of splendors and
delights." She reads French history, longs for "a great
poet of the Southland — to mourn suitably for our dead,"
and enjoys "learned music — Wagner's stuff and that
sort of thing." Her disguised husband — De Forest has

removed the false whiskers donned in a darkened church ceremony — talks of aesthetics while at the Luxembourg, and observes that "art doesn't spring up in thinly settled agricultural districts. It needs cities."

IV

Commissioned as a captain in Company I of the Twelfth Connecticut Volunteers, The Charter Oak Regiment, De Forest steeped himself in the Civil War:

> Counting service in war and in peace, I was six and a half years under the colors. I was in three storming parties, six days of field engagement, and thirty-seven days of siege duty, making forty-six days under fire.
>
> My chief regret with regard to this matter is that I could not take part in one of the greater battles, such as Gettysburg or Chickamauga. I am not only glad, but I am sincerely thankful that I did not miss Port Hudson and the final victories in the Shenandoah Valley. In the finishing fight there I was on the staff of General Emory, carrying various orders for him and one for General Sheridan.

These years he told in letters home, with revelation of life on military transports, drunkenness in camp (*A Lover's Revolt* includes strong scenes of the troops of General Gage swilling four-penny quarts of New England rum), the haphazard commissary, initial exposure to fire and death at Georgia Landing and the assaults on Port Hudson where he was wounded. Retold in his later assignment to write Nineteenth Corps history, at last they merged into *Miss Ravenel's Conversion.* The war-spared Howells returned again and again to this novel, discovering that "it does not shrink even when put by the side of Tolstoi's *War and Peace.*" For De Forest was one of the first to avoid what he called the false, "the poetical view of battle. (If you want to know how a hero feels in the trenches get behind a tree not quite big enough to cover you.)" He chose to catalog items like the terror of Port Hudson, surgery in the field hospitals, the waking of Carter's brigade at Cane River, the constant wish for promotion, the passing of time by the brave with free whiskey and easy women. But he lived to see greater popularity than his country ever gave him bestowed upon the war novel of a boy not yet born when he was feverish and hungry in Louisiana and Virginia. He also lived to read "The Open Boat" and know how superbly Crane handled a shipwreck like that at the start of *Kate Beaumont.*

It is not only in the campaigns of *Miss Ravenel's Conversion* and the cavalry operations and night skirmishes of *Overland* that De Forest shows his stature as a war novelist. The first readers of the manuscript of *A Lover's Revolt* ranked it with *The Spy* and S. Weir Mitchell's *Hugh Wynne,* for *A Lover's Revolt* recreates with authority the "first battle-day of the American Revolution"; we have no better treatment of Lexington and the assault on Bunker Hill. It gives the "little touches" he admired in Tolstoi — a cherry-cheeked boy and his father — as well as the technical details: the strategic plan of battle and the tactical ebb and flow; a careful exposition of terrain, tables of organization, drill systems, maneuvers, uniforms, weapons, ammunition, staff organization — even the books and "spoken English" of the colonial troops. When Howells introduced him to the Russian, he recognized at once with his veteran's memory the scope of the epic writer:

> You do right to praise Tolstoi. Something that you wrote a while ago sent me to *Peace and War.* . . .

Let me tell you that nobody but he has written the whole truth about war and battle. I tried, and I told all I dared, and perhaps all I could. But there was one thing I did not dare tell, lest the world should infer that I was naturally a coward, and so could not know the feelings of a brave man. I actually did not dare state the extreme horror of battle, and the anguish with which the bravest soldiers struggle through it. His story of Borodino — the soldiers sitting hungry and white under the storm of death; the desperate struggles to keep away from the horrors of the situation; the poor brave Prince pacing the meadow, counting his steps . . . it is the actual truth about the glories of war. I say it on the faith of a man who has seen it all a great many times by the hour together. . . . Oddly enough, the truth is not true to the uninformed. I recommended Tolstoi's *Borodino* to an educated, bright man. . . . He returned it with the remark that it seemed 'confused.' Well, that is just the truth, the super-eminent, vital fact of the description. Nothing is more confounding, fragmentary, incomprehensible than a battle as one sees it. And you see so little, too, unless you are a staff officer and ride about, or perhaps a general. No two spectators ever fully agree in their story of a battle. Tolstoi must have been engaged many times. There are a thousand little touches which nobody could have guessed . . . touches which go to make up the picture of the haste, flurry, confusion, which a battle is. I am glad to have found Tolstoi.

After *Miss Ravenel's Conversion* his productivity, if not his popularity, gathered momentum as the 1860's ended. The name of De Forest over serialized novels, short stories, essays, and poetry appeared often in *Harper's*, *Galaxy*, and thanks to Howells' (September 1868) invitation to send manuscripts, in *The Atlantic*; thirty years later Howells continued to place De Forest with publishers. The New Haven man competed for space and readers with famous English writers like Thackeray, Dickens, Wilkie Collins, Trollope, and emerging Americans like Henry James and Mark Twain. The technical demands and restrictions of magazine publication perturbed him as they sometimes did Dickens. To overcome the forced patterning into brief scenes of equal length, a common structural fault of the period, according to Alexander Cowie, he thought "the number had better be long than short," but obedient to Howells' editorial demands he shortened the last installments of *Kate Beaumont*. Later when he received proofs of another novel, he complained that the printers had "rammed" his narrative and dialogue into solid columns. "An author's paragraphing is part of his style; and mine is meant to help the reader understand and take notice." An extant letter to Donald Grant Mitchell (1870) shows his response to editorial finicality:

> I think that I have removed all the rocks of offence; if not, please give them a hasty dig yourself, showing no tenderness. I have cut out, as far as may be without destroying sense, all such words as slavery, freedom and other banner words; and I have softened or removed allusions to local peculiarities. Moreover, I have interpolated the accompanying passages. You see that they represent the objects of my fun (if it be fun) as eccentrics, odd fish, and not representatives of the classes to which they belong. It seems to me that this ought to obviate the rancor of both radical and silver-grey.

Out of his knowledge of the South before Sumter and two years' experience as an administrator in South Carolina for the Bureau of Freedmen and Refugees came short fiction like that real foreshadowing of Caldwell and Faulkner, "An Independent KuKlux," with Selnarten Bowen, his quid-chewing wife, and the Negro Ham, who, like Major Scott in *Miss Ravenel's Conversion*, is "much in the habit of matrimony." "Drawing Bureau Rations" is one of his episodes of social fragmentation everywhere evident in his wide, war-ravished area. The major accomplishment of years among the poor-white "low-down-ers" and an earlier, unbroken Southern society is *Kate Beaumont*, according to his most appreciative early critic, Clarence Gordon in 1873, "the most prominent, the most popular, and probably the best of Mr. De Forest's works." Those who want evidence of pioneer realism should read the chapters composed long before Howells' Bartley Hubbard went on his polite, hot-scotch spree, that take Randolph Armitage, "one of those knight-errants who are created by the accolade of a bottle," to the cracker ball, and blind drunk on raw corn, back to his wife:

"I wonder at you," said Kate once. "I never imagined that a woman could have such fortitude."

"Fortitude!" returned Nellie. "I am intelligent enough to know that it is not fortitude that you mean. It is mere hardened callousness and want of feeling. I ceased some time ago to be a woman. I am a species of brute."

But fame continued to elude De Forest even with frequent publication. He told Howells in 1871,

> I was almost discouraged the other day by a leader in the Tribune on "American Novels" which said that De Forest is doing good work "almost unnoticed." I see few papers, but I fear the man is right. If you think so, let me know and I will try to put in more stimulus, or, that failing, to be much briefer. Perhaps, however, the coming volume publication of Overland will help. In this country advertisement and trumpeting are as potent as around Jericho.

Howells in an 1872 "Recent Literature" column that also treated *The Hoosier Schoolmaster*, told his readers that with *Miss Ravenel's Conversion* and *Overland, Kate Beaumont* "forms to our minds, strong proof that we are not so much lacking in an American novelist as in a public to recognize him." But that year Lippincott printed *Not Pretty, But Precious,* a collection of short fiction by "John Hay, Clara F. Guernsey, Margaret Hosmer, Harriet Prescott Spofford, Lucy Hamilton Hooper, Etc." De Forest had not yet achieved equal billing with the four ladies; he is the "Etc." on the title page.

V

It is revealing that when De Forest in 1868 wrote a study of the American novel, with *Uncle Tom's Cabin* he cited *Little Dorrit* rather than any other work by Dickens. Like Shaw he sensed its power to reform. Later he could not read enough of Zola. Like Dickens, Stowe, and Charles Reade with whom Howells and others compared him — *The Nation* in 1874 called De Forest an American Charles Reade — beginning with *Witching Times* he had built his fiction on a cause. He had ended this rendering of a society nearly destroyed by total magisterial tyranny — a primitive *1984* or *Darkness at Noon* — with a charge:

> Let all future Cotton Mathers learn charity from his unintentional sins, and the mortifying inevitable manner in which they found him out. For, if there is any lesson to be drawn from this book, it is, that even in such a trinity as faith, hope, and charity, the greatest and most beautiful thing of all is charity.

In *Miss Ravenel's Conversion* he had exposed the speculators, the financial camp followers who made deals with Colonel Carter for cotton and government riverboats; Ben Butler's application of Washington politics to New

Orleans, damaging to the Union troops and helpful to enemy civilians; the promotions like Gazaway's through political pressure when Carter wanted the coward disgraced and gibbeted. (De Forest himself ended his military career as a brevet-major — slow advance for so long a tour of duty.) A large part of the narrative scheme of *Kate Beaumont* contains the progress of a congressional campaign in South Carolina complete with partisans and "wire-pullers."

In "The Colored Member," a story printed in *Galaxy*, March 1872, he came to the railroad lobbyist and the fraudulent promoter. Daddy Abel, who looks like a turkey buzzard, announces the theme when he tells Jack Hunt, the carpetbagger lobbyist, "they's heaps o' money in this railroading business o' yourn." Pompey, the colored member of a Southern legislature, gets drunk on free liquor, tells off the lobbyist and suffers the consequence of his patriotic indiscretion. His seat is promptly contested, taken from him, and he is returned to private life in Alligatorville, to his 'possums and sweet potatoes. In December 1872 *The Atlantic* ran "An Inspired Lobbyist," with settings familiar to John Vane: the town of Slowburg (he added an "h" in the novel) in "a little state, which may have been Rhode Island, or may have been Connecticut"; and two Washington command posts: the bar of the Arlington Hotel and the committee rooms of the Capitol. The inspired lobbyist, Ananias Pullwool, succeeds in making the citizens of Fastburg hire him to lobby their town into becoming the sole capital of the little state, rather than continue sharing honors with Slowburg. After Pullwool pockets Fastburg money he moves to its rival and raises money there to halt Fastburg's plan. The result for the duped towns is a stalemate; Pullwool is the only winner.

The Credit Mobilier was too massive a fraud to crowd into a short story. Though the genre of the political novel had only been touched by the early 1870's, De Forest attempted in *Honest John Vane* to go beyond the partial treatment of his early fiction and write a total political novel. For the first time his major character would be a politician active in Washington. There were few American guides: Brackenridge's *Modern Chivalry* had remained isolated for half a century; then with the pulse of realism quickening, the Brook Farmer G. W. Curtis in *Trumps* (1861), turned his reforming zeal to corporate influence on legislation and legislators. A New York journalist, Henry Morford, in 1863 and 1864 wrote three novels of the corruption spread by army contractors with their paper shoes and rotten meat. In England, Disraeli had added *Lothair* (1870) to the three political novels with which he pioneered in the 1840's. More important for De Forest than the existence in literature of a character like the Etonian aristocrat Coningsby, to the genre came Trollope with his political aspirations, months as an observer in the galleries of the House of Commons, campaign experience, and anger over evidence of degradation among the electorate. The American read carefully the six Parliamentary novels beginning with *Can You Forgive Her* (1864), where we meet the great Liberal, Plantagenet Palliser, and the publican Mr. Grimes, who equates votes with hard cash. *Phineas Finn* (1869), like the Slowburgh aspirant, is helped to victory by the involvement of a rival in bribery. The satirical *Eustace Diamonds* (1873), serialized earlier in the same issues of *Galaxy* with De Forest material, contains in the wicked Lady Eustace a woman whose way of life Olympia Vane and Josephine Murray understand. *Honest John Vane, Playing The Mischief,* and *Justine's Lovers* may be considered De Forest's attempt to parallel Trollope and write an American Congressional series.

He continued to use national political subjects to the very end of his career. *A Lover's Revolt* with its ideological conflict between Rebel and Tory, ends with the triumph of the former seen as a portent: A family loyal to the King "were so busy with the poor old Tory body of death that they missed seeing Major Asahel Farnlee ride past . . . his black eyes sparkling and his dark aquiline face flushed with triumph, an incarnation of the coming republic." *The Downing Legends,* at the start of the new century, are of American "manifest destiny" in a "whimsical guise." *Medley and Palestina* (1902) contains the ballad of a logrolling Congressman, "Judge Boodle."

De Forest was by no means the one native novelist of his generation to become absorbed in a new subject. Twain's full-length study of contemporary history is the irreverent *Gilded Age.* Henry Adams' anonymous *Democracy* (1880) ran through sixteen editions, readers preferring his Mrs. Lightfoot Lee to Mrs. Vane and Mrs. Murray. Albion Tourgée also used the Credit Mobilier. Hamlin Garland, Marion Crawford, Frank Norris, Winston Churchill, David Graham Phillips — in turn at his New Haven hotel the long-lived De Forest (he died 6 June 1906) watched the authors of successors to his *Honest John Vane* and *Playing The Mischief* succumb as he had to the excitement of attempting to master a fictional form and subject described by an English practitioner, Mrs. Humphry Ward, as most difficult of all but also the most tempting to the mature artist. De Forest would have welcomed *Of Thee I Sing* and *The Last Hurrah.*

VI

"Did Mr. De Forest," asked *The Nation*, "refresh his memory of Swift before writing the adventures of John Vane?" Though he knew his *Gulliver* ("Brobdingnagian" is his epithet as far back as *Witching Times*), he testified here as he did in *Playing The Mischief* where he called the United States "this great model republic of Vanity Fair," that Bunyan rather than Swift served as his mentor in allegory as the Puritan had served Hawthorne. Describing in his twenty-third chapter the widening web of guilt spun by the vindictive testimony of Simon Sharp, he wrote, "It was a new and perversely reversed and altogether bedevilled rendering of the *Pilgrim's Progress* into American politics; it was much as if Bunyan had at last pitched *his* Christian and Hopeful into the little buried hole which led from the gate of Zion to the Pit."

Without forcing the novel into a false, rigid analogy, it is possible to follow John Vane to his "reversed" goal. He journeys not to the holy city of Zion, but to Destruction, with profitable excursions to the Valley of Ease where the silver mines are accessible. Like Pliable he is converted by Darius Dorman, who is De Forest's version of the "foul fiend" Apollyon. Vane listens all the woeful way to the false Evangelists, to Simon Sharp, to Senator Ironman, that Beelzebub who in flesh may have been Zachariah Chandler of Michigan whose H Street house mounted many parties like the one Olympia longed to attend — though she had but the garnet gown. Or Roscoe Conkling, the foppish Senator from New York, may have sat for Ironman. It was Conkling who fathered the strategy described in *Honest John Vane* of a suspect legislator introducing a resolution of inquiry into corruption which involved himself, and then dominating the appointments to the investigating committee. A newspaper from Conkling's home state dared print without fear of a libel suit the charge that his great wealth had all accrued after he reached Washington. Nor is Olympia Vane to travel like Christiana; she is fated to remain the daughter Adam called Pride of Life.

De Forest's retention of Bunyan's prototypes for his allegory, and his reversal of Christian's direction from good to evil prevented the novel from having either hero or heroine. With few minor exceptions the author is instantly hostile to all of his characters, revealing his scornful bias through slanted editorial statement, rather than risking ambiguity by definition in dramatic scene or through narrative reflection. His voice, always heard guiding the reader's sensibilities and forming his loyalties, is as overt as a cartoonist's — his contemporary Nast who was blackening similar subjects, or Matt Morgan of *Leslie's* or Darley, whose plates De Forest used in the *History of the Indians of Connecticut*. From the beginning, indeed with the ironic symbol and pun of the title — he had also punned in *Miss Ravenel* with Larue when he meant *La rouée* — he prepares the reader for Vane's ultimate foundering in the Washington slough. The Slowburgh citizen possessed a good name, but De Forest tells us that it was bought cheaply and used vainly. At first glance a man of stature, he is soon denigrated physically by jibes that he "ran a little too much to blubber for comfort" and that he was "slightly vacuous in expression." Lest doubt remain as to his opinion of the Congressman, De Forest summarizes him as a man who "had no moral or intellectual significance. . . . He did not prize virtue for its own sake but because the name of it had brought him honor." Lack of character and ideals negates the evolutionary process and produces a leader manqué.

The author's handling of handsome Olympia Vane makes her something less than endearing. She had been "polished by long-continued friction against undergraduate pundits." (In *Seacliff*, where he tells of a college junior who is a lifelong sophomore, in *Miss Ravenel's Conversion*, with its town and gown touches, in *Honest John Vane*, and in *Irene The Missionary*, De Forest pioneers the use of the campus in fiction.) She knows what it is to stay up after midnight unchaperoned and to be engaged often, for she is in danger of becoming like the belle who "hung on to the students till she was well into the thirties," Miss Minnie Biffles of *Irene The Missionary*, "a college widow — that's what we used to call them." Her mother, "industrially and morally," is "worth six" of Olympia. Mrs. Smiles, the hard-pressed boarding-house hostess who "had come out at the little end of the horn of plenty," is the one woman De Forest touches with respect; his tribute to her comes out of his travel memories for she reminds him of weathered Italian statuary. The younger sister gets little traditional sentiment. She appears briefly and is removed quickly, not by tearful death as in the novels of Augusta Evans Wilson or Susan Warner but by watchful Olympia, who recognizes a possible rival for favor in the "china-ware blue eyes" of the erstwhile manufacturer of refrigerators and takes prompt remedial action.

In *Miss Ravenel's Conversion* De Forest deliberately turned away from the Charles O'Malley type of military character; in *Honest John Vane* he avoided any similarity to a recent success like Faith in *Gates Ajar*, with twenty printings in one year, or Gertrude of *The Lamplighter*, with hundreds of thousands of American and English buyers. Nor does John ever see his Olympia as Don Quixote saw Dulcinea, the beautiful figment in the book De Forest read as lovingly and as frequently as the *Pilgrim's Progress* and *The Arabian Nights.* Olympia is a fleshly reality who will not tolerate a time of two small rooms and travel by horse-cars with a husband who rates only minor committee assignments. "Is it possible," he asked himself, "that she is not going to be satisfied with succeeding through *my* success but means to make her own glory the centre of our life?" Olympia becomes "sore and prickly with a consciousness of her husband's incapacity," and John, who might have followed the advice and example of the idealist-reformer, the "revenue tariff" crusader Cavendish, to remain honest though it meant a life of "tough steak and cold hominy of cheap boarding houses," sells a reputation worth more than its original one hundred dollars to his Mephistopheles not to possess Marguerite but to silence her.

We also see the Vanes from another perspective, that of *Playing The Mischief* where they reappear, for De Forest, like Trollope with Palliser and Lady Glencora, carried some of his characters into later books. The second meeting confirms the first. The Congressman is now a well-known ten percenter, all show of dedicated statesmanship long fled from his fatted conscience. He can afford to dine at John Welcker's walnut-panelled restaurant, with its framed letter from Charles Dickens praising the superlative cuisine. His companions are veterans of the Credit Mobilier who plan other raids; in fact the Great Subfluvial and the Sub-Tunnel, corporate names De Forest used for legal and artistic reasons rather than their archetypes, the Union Pacific and the Credit Mobilier, are both composites of two actual wildcat schemes of the day: a drainage tunnel under the Comstock Lode and a plan to save "the alluvial" running into the Gulf of Mexico. The "semi-vulgar" Olympia is a fixture at Senator Ironman's parties, the elegant target of new favor seekers. Physically she remains a "lovely woman" but her character is "of the greedy, extravagant, envious, spiteful sort."

With Darius Dorman, De Forest risked violating the advice of his own young author in *Seacliff:* "Poor novelists and playwrights are perpetually caricaturing real life, with a faith in human stupidity which pays us no compliment." And some of his readers, including Howells and James, called him for forcing the concept. He had first sketched Dorman in a short story with the obvious name of Professor Heller. Now he modelled his embellished satanic iconography not only after Bunyan's Apollyon, but the personification of evil by other titans: Milton and Goethe. One reviewer sensed a turning to Hawthorne. Indeed Goodman Brown had walked in the forest with the sooty Dorman, though he knew him as "the traveller with the twisted staff."

Job Poor (Pennsylvania's "Pig Iron" Kelley of high-tariff notoriety?), "such fellows as Christian and Faithful in the Senate . . . Greatheart and Hopeful in the House" are all Dorman's creatures, fit representatives of an electorate that cannot vote for a Bummer because he violated the "cardinal eleventh commandment, Thou shalt not be found out"; and will not vote for a Saltonstall because he is "too much of a gentleman." They settle for a John Vane. De Forest's scorn for all of this is Carlylean, his irritation as obvious as that other experienced Washington observer, Whitman of *Democratic Vistas*, who was insisting that the obvious ills of American society must undergo sharp diagnosis.

"As long as these subsidy bills and relief bills are allowed," observes Greatheart, "no man ought to run for Congress who is not a Croesus or a Cato." But the candidate from Slowburgh is neither rich nor wise.

In terms of popular fiction ground out by the Mrs. Wilson, Southworth, Phelps, Warner, and the star of De Forest's former publishers, Annie Edwardes, whose seven novels Sheldon & Co. blurbed as ranking with George Eliot's — soon to be joined by E. P. Roe who proved that sentiment and piety profited a male novelist more than satire and the muck-rake — De Forest could have been accused of writing an anti-novel. He offered the common reader little: no hero, no heroine, only villains and villainy on a national scale and the disturbing sound of a reformer lecturing to the heedless. No romance for the patrons of American Mudie's Select Library, but "an entire absence of sentimentality," gross men, gratuitous insults to contemporary women. He preferred those of older times, "when ladies were not mere dandies," but "like their men, were producers as well as consumers." (This disdain revealed itself in *The Wetherel Affair* where Alice Dinneford like "many another 'sweet girl' of our times . . . had grown up in the belief that life ought to be one everlasting picnic, at least for young ladies.") For his efforts he got as little support as Horace Greeley, who like John Vane and Twain's Senator Dilworthy, also fought the franking privilege in the pathetic campaign of 1872. The American public was as unready for De Forest's concept of the political novel, told with his "twin honesties, moral and mental," as Clarence Gordon named them, as it was for reform presidents. He scoffed at Jacob Abbott's "instructive juveniles," but they sold in the millions. Richmond &

Patten's one edition of *Honest John Vane* has sufficed all these years.

Earlier magazine publication of the novel linking him to *The Atlantic* school lessened the likelihood of reviews in other periodicals; the first extensive review did not help sales. In all of his fiction he sought to avoid writing like the amateur litterateur he described in *Kate Beaumont*: "a kind of poetical prose, much admired by some of the women to whom he read it." He hated language "worn threadbare" and showing "all the seams and creases." Nor did he treat tolerantly his characters who talked "in what Blair calls 'full periods.'" When he classed Caesar's *Commentaries* as the best of all military narratives, he spoke of "its extreme simplicity and naturalness of manner." Caesar never "struts" and has an "apparent scorn of mere diction"; no prose could be less given to "points and artifices of rhetoric." Dr. Ravenel uses the verb "tote" because it has "a monosyllabic vigor about it which pleads for it." The writing in *Honest John Vane* is, then, purposely understated, dead-pan, until enlivened by gusts of sardonic wit as startling as the extended figure of the now-venal Congressman rolled over like a crab and submerged by the flood of lobby-created corruption. De Forest included editorial-like paragraphs such as those on the members of the "spiritual mobocracy," and frequent gags or "hits," like "He learned, or supposed he had learned, that many Congressmen kept Uncle Sam's eagle setting on their own financial eggs." Or "Darius smiled, as a slave-trader might smile upon a stalwart, unsuspicious negro who should express a curiosity to see the interior of his schooner." He used the unexpected, ironic epithet: "It cost him seconds of penal meditation"; and phrases like "thimbleful of soul." It can be said of De Forest in *Honest John Vane* what he wrote of Bentley Armitage in *Kate Beaumont*: "one side of his face all seriousness, and the other full of satire."

But now he was found "decidedly turbid" and guilty of "loose writing and coarse imagery." Henry James in *The Nation* for 31 December 1874, granted that "the portrait of one of our . . . usual legislators . . . has a great deal of force," but concluded with this assault:

> Whether accidentally or intentionally we hardly know, "Honest John Vane" exhales a penetrating aroma of what in plain English one must call vulgarity. Every note the author strikes reverberates with a peculiarly vulgar tone; vulgarity pervades the suggestions, the atmosphere of his volume. This result has doubtless been in a great measure designed; he has wished to overwhelm the reader with the evil odor of lobbyism. But the reader, duly overwhelmed, and laying down the volume with a sense of having been in irredeemably low company, may be excused for wondering whether, if this were a logical symbol of American civilization, it would not be well to let that phenomenon be submerged in the tide of corruption.

Howells, already on record in the belief that De Forest "is really the only American novelist" (1874), came to his side in *The Atlantic* for February 1875 — an issue that carried parts of *Roderick Hudson* and *Old Times on the Mississippi*:

> You have but to change names and dates a very little, and you have the Congressional Washington of 1874-1875 as clearly portrayed in the book as that of 1871-1872. In this country, at least, there has never been so good a political satire as this; but its excellence as a political satire is only one of the many excellencies in it. The principal persons, John Vane and his wife, are presented with the sharpness and

depth of delineation which one finds in all of Mr.
De Forest's best work, and which is peculiar to him.

Olympia Vane brought special praise from the editor:

> She is to be added to that line of women in the
> painting of whom Mr. De Forest — never weak in
> the presentation of character — would be recognized
> by a more discerning public than ours, as having
> shown the skill and force of a master. Whether they
> are pleasant people or not is quite beside the pur-
> pose. One feels them to be true, and that is enough.

Howells' tribute culminated years later in *A Modern
Instance*. Had Olympia Vane travelled from Washington to Equity, Maine — and by then her husband's wages
allowed a special car — she would have been at home
with Marcia Gaylord. In the letter that De Forest considered "the soundest praise I ever had," Howells in 1886
wrote him:

> I ought to tell you that it was your bold grappling
> with the fact of the robust lovemaking among three-
> fourths of our nation that gave me courage to deal
> with it in Lemuel, and a Modern Instance. It's odd
> that no one touched it before you. But our life, as
> it differs from that of other nations, is as yet almost
> wholly untouched in our fiction. You I consider our
> earliest *novelist*.

Other strengths of *Honest John Vane* could have been
noted. Thackerayan intrusions sometimes damage the
tone of earlier books. Here they are reduced or masked
with selective skill. The plot avoids cumbrous episodes,
fashionable sub-plots and inserts, the contrived, install-
ment-ending suspense that mars *Overland*, or the re-
course to coincidence of *Miss Ravenel's Conversion*. It
has a direct, inevitable flow that is like a simple, clarified abstract of the voluminous testimony given to the

Forty-Second Congress. And yet individual sections emerge: Dorman's analysis of the repudiation of Saltonstall by the party hacks: "You can't get people to hurrah for a gravestone, even if it has a fine name on it"; the night of the caucus and the itemizing of Vane's platform; the summary of post-war political economy; Congressman Simon Sharp's exposition of "usefulness" and "special legislation"; the discussion of the lobby-corrupted legislators after Vane utters his first words of sin, "Darius, I am awfully hard up"; the study of that "partially respectable statesman and almost entirely ludicrous man," Senator Ironman; the quick descent of Vane after his discovery, as painful an epiphany as Goodman Brown's sight of Faith's pink ribbon, that "the other respected temples of righteousness, were nothing but whited sepulchres, full of railroad bonds and all uncleanness"; and the transformation of the hesitant sinner into a predatory conniver:

> "I don't see how I came to make this blunder," he chattered, arching his eyebrows as apologetical monkeys do. [Dorman had withheld a dividend.]
>
> "You don't pronounce it right; it wasn't a blunder, but plunder," smiled Vane, with a satirical severity, suggestive of Satan rebuking Sin.

Even James liked the narrative strategy that guided Vane through the confrontation by the investigators and inspired his escape. "Mr. De Forest did well not to sacrifice to the vulgar need for a dénouement, but to leave his hero's subsequent career to the irritated conscience of the reader."

The most flagrant error of reviewers was to miss De Forest's affirmation that the "vast, industrious decent American public, which wire-pullers usually regard as having no more intelligence or more principle than one of the forces of nature, showed unmistakably that it possessed much political virtue and some political sense." Nor could his contemporaries appreciate his prophetic concern over the longevity of the lobby. At the end of *Honest John Vane* De Forest disposed of his Satan, his Darius Dorman, "who vanished and was not seen." But news out of Washington the many years since the Credit Mobilier tells us of Dorman's occasional return. Until he is gone forever, *Honest John Vane* deserves a reading.

JOSEPH JAY RUBIN
THE PENNSYLVANIA STATE UNIVERSITY

☞ SOURCES

ACKNOWLEDGMENTS

Gordon S. Haight has done for De Forest in this century what Howells tried earlier: reprint a major novel and proclaim its author's underrated work in introductions to *Miss Ravenel's Conversion* (1939 and 1955) and his chapter "Realism Defined" in the *Literary History of the United States*. James H. Croushore's valuable editions of *A Volunteer's Adventures* (New Haven, 1946) and *A Union Officer in the Reconstruction* (New Haven, 1948), contain introductions by Stanley T. Williams and David M. Potter; both volumes testify to the depth of De Forest's experience. Three historians: Arthur H. Quinn, *American Fiction* (New York, 1936), Alexander Cowie, *The Rise of the American Novel* (New York, 1951), and Edward Wagenknecht, *Cavalcade of the American Novel* (New York, 1952), have amplified the judgment of Howells recorded in 1895:

> I have long thought it more discreditable to our taste than to his talent that he has not been recognized as one of our foremost novelists, for his keen and accurate touch in character, his wide scope, and his unerring rendition of whatever he has attempted to report of American life.

The official source of information about the Credit Mobilier is the *Reports of Committees of the House of Representatives for the Third Session of the Forty-Sec-*

ond Congress (Washington, 1873). George A. Townsend, *Washington Outside and Inside* (Hartford, 1874); Henry K. White, *History of the Union Pacific Railway* (Chicago, 1895); Nelson Trottman, *History of the Union Pacific* (New York, 1923); and Fletcher M. Green, "Origins of the Credit Mobilier of America," *Mississippi Valley Historical Review* (September 1959), 238-251, add to the sorry revelations.

I wish to thank Yale University Library for permission to examine and reprint from its extensive collection of De Forest letters, manuscripts, and books; and Harvard University Library for copies of letters to Howells. The quotations from the letters of Howells to De Forest are printed with the permission of the heirs of William Dean Howells; further use may not be made by others without express permission. The Pennsylvania State University provided a research grant, and its Fred Lewis Pattee Library offered facilities and materials. Three of my colleagues, Ira V. Brown, Arthur O. Lewis, and Hadly R. Waters, read sections of the manuscript and offered suggestions.

Finally, it is a pleasant duty to record gratitude to Harrison T. Meserole for his many hours of editorial help.

☞ *TEXT*

With the exception of silent changes made for the sake of standardizing spelling, capitalization, punctuation, and correcting obvious misprints — or an auctorial slip like the writing of Jabez for Simon — the text of *Honest John Vane* reproduced here is that of the only book edition, published in 1875 by Richmond & Patten, New Haven. Since its first appearance in five installments of *The Atlantic Monthly* from July through November 1873, De Forest had made approximately fifty minor changes in the text of the novel. He added a table of contents, clarified chapter designations, and touched some of the tag lines; he substituted phrases and single words: "feeding place" became "hash house"; "as," "that," "towards," "cheering," became "so," "this," "toward," and "cheeringly"; and he removed a reference to the non-smoking Vane lighting a cigar. No version of *Honest John Vane* with extensive revisions comparable to those he made in *Miss Ravenel's Conversion, Kate Beaumont,* and *Playing The Mischief* exists among the De Forest manuscripts now preserved in Yale University Library.

Receiving the author's signature on their contract 23 September 1874, Richmond & Patten before the end of the year produced one of the best-printed of De Forest's novels. The small 4½ x 7 volume of 259 pages, bound in dark orange cloth with the title stamped in thick gilt on spine and side, avoided the many irritating misprints of *Miss Ravenel's Conversion,* the double columns of *Kate Beaumont* and *Playing The Mischief,* and the small type of *Overland.* But the New Haven firm met the fate of De Forest's earlier New York and Boston publishers, for Richmond & Patten also went bankrupt and suspended publication.

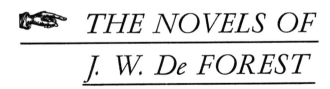

THE NOVELS OF
J. W. De FOREST

<table>
<tr><td>WITCHING TIMES</td><td>1856</td></tr>
<tr><td>SEACLIFF</td><td>1859</td></tr>
<tr><td>MISS RAVENEL'S CONVERSION</td><td>1867</td></tr>
<tr><td>OVERLAND</td><td>1871</td></tr>
<tr><td>KATE BEAUMONT</td><td>1872</td></tr>
<tr><td>THE WETHEREL AFFAIR</td><td>1873</td></tr>
<tr><td>HONEST JOHN VANE</td><td>1875</td></tr>
<tr><td>PLAYING THE MISCHIEF</td><td>1875</td></tr>
<tr><td>JUSTINE'S LOVERS</td><td>1878</td></tr>
<tr><td>IRENE THE MISSIONARY</td><td>1879</td></tr>
<tr><td>THE BLOODY CHASM</td><td>1881</td></tr>
<tr><td>A LOVER'S REVOLT</td><td>1898</td></tr>
</table>

The date after each novel, with the exception of *Witching Times,* is that of first book publication.

HONEST JOHN VANE

CONTENTS

ONE of the most fateful days of John Vane's life was the day on which he took board with that genteel though decayed lady, the widow of a wholesale New York grocer who had come out at the little end of the horn of plenty, and the mother of two of the prettiest girls in Slowburgh, Mrs. Renssaelaer Smiles.

Within a week he was in a state of feeling which made him glance frequently at the eldest of these young ladies, and within a month he would have jumped at a chance to kiss the ground upon which she trod. In the interval he ventured various little attentions, intended to express his growing admiration and interest, such as opening the door for her when she left the dining-room, taking off his hat with a flourish when he met her in the hall, joining her now and then in the street, "just for a block or two," and once tremulously presenting her with a bouquet.

He would have been glad to run much more boldly than this in the course of courtship, but his heart was in such a tender-footed condition that he could not go otherwise than softly. In his worshiping eyes Miss Olympia Smiles was not only a lovely phenomenon, but also an august and even an absolutely imposing one. Notwithstanding that she was the daughter of his landlady, and held but a modest social position even in our unpretentious little city, she had an unmistakable air of fashionable breeding and boarding-school finish, such as might be expected of a lady who had passed her early youth in opulence. Moreover, she drew about her an admiring bevy of our university undergraduates, who, by their genteel fopperies and classic witticisms, made Vane feel ill at ease in their presence, although he strove manfully in secret to despise them as mere boys. Finally, she was handsome and impressively so, tall, shapely, and grand in figure, superb and even haughty in carriage, with a rich brunette coloring which made him think of Cleopatra, and with glowing dark eyes which pierced even to his joints and marrow.

The one circumstance which encouraged Vane to aspire after this astral being was the fact that she seemed older than most of the undergraduate planets who revolved about her, throwing him for the present into sorrowful eclipse. He thought that she must be twenty-three, and he sometimes trusted that she might be twenty-five, or perhaps twenty-seven. At the same time he so reverenced her that he could not have been tortured into believing that she was a veteran flirt, trained to tough coquetry in many a desperate skirmish. Often and often had Olympia "sat up" with a young man till after midnight, and then gone up stairs and passed her mother's bedroom door on her hands and knees, not in penance and mortification of spirit, but in mere anxiety to escape a lecture.

Of these melodramatic scenes John Vane knew nothing, and desired to know nothing. We must add also, as indicative of his character and breeding, that, had he been minutely informed of them, he would have thought none the less of Miss Smiles. In the first place he was so fascinated by her that he would have pardoned almost any folly or imprudence in her bygone history. In the second place, he had been brought up in a simple stratum of society, where girls were allowed large liberties in sparking, even to the extent of arms around the waist and much kissing, without incurring prudish condemnation. Indeed, so far was he from being fastidious in these matters, that, when he heard that Olympia had been engaged to one or more students, and that these juvenile bonds had been promptly severed, he was rather pleased and cheered by the information than otherwise.

"She must be about sick of those young jackanapes," he hopefully inferred. "She must be about ready to take up with a grown man, who knows what he wants, and has some notion of sticking to a bargain, and is able to do the decent thing in the way of supporting her."

John Vane was himself, both in person and in repute, no despicable match. As may have been already guessed by such readers as are fitted to apprehend his character and find instruction in his history, he was one of those heroes of industry and conquerors of circumstances known as self-made men, whose successes are so full of encouragement to the millions born into mediocrity, and whom, consequently, those millions delight to honor.

Had he really fabricated himself, whether we speak of his physical structure or of his emotional nature, he would have accomplished a rather praiseworthy job of creation. Very few better looking men or kinder hearted men have ever paraded the streets of Slowburgh in Masonic caparisons. Justly proportioned, with ample withers, a capacious barrel, and limbs that were almost majestic, he stood nearly six feet high in his stockings, weighed full two hundred pounds in the same, and was altogether an uncommonly fine animal. It is true that, to use his own jovial phrase, he "ran a little too much to blubber for comfort"; but it was disposed so becomingly and carried so easily, that it did not prevent him from moving with grace; while even his political enemies had to admit that it conspicuously enhanced his dignity, and justified his admirers in talking of him for governor.

His face, too, usually passed for handsome; it was fairly regular in feature, and of a fresh blonde color like that of a healthy baby; moreover, it had the spiritual embellishment of a ready, courteous, and kindly smile. It was only the fastidiously aristocratic and the microscopically cultivated who remarked of this large and well-moulded figure-head that it lacked an air of high-breeding and was slightly vacuous in expression. These severe critics found the genial blue eyes which fascinated humble people as uninteresting as if they had been made of china-ware. They hinted, in short, that John Vane's beauty was purely physical, and had no moral or intellectual significance.

To this height of sentimental fault-finding Miss Olympia Smiles had not attained. New-Yorker by birth though she was, and polished by long-continued friction against undergraduate pundits, she was not a soul of the last and most painful finish. She could not see but that Mr. Vane was, from every point of view, sufficiently handsome. Still she did not feel much pleased with his obvious admiration, nor desire at all to lure him on to the point of love-making. There were imperfections in him which grated upon her sensibilities, far as these were from being feverishly delicate.

In the first place, she found his conversation rather uninteresting and distinctly "common." He could only talk freely of politics, business, and the ordinary news of the day; he had no sparkles of refined wit and no warm flashes of poesy; he was a little given to coarse chaffing and to slang. For instance, he one day said to his *vis-à-vis* at table, "Harris, please to scull that butter over this way"; and, what made the matter worse, he said it with a self-satisfied smile, as though the phrase were original and irresistibly humorous. It was unpleasant also to hear him remark every morning, alluding to the severity of the weather, that "the thermometer was on a bender." Such metaphors might do in students and other larkish, agreeable youngsters; but in a mature man, who pretended to be marriageable, they argued dullness or vulgarity. Finally, Olympia plainly gathered from Mr. Vane's daily discourse that he was pretty ignorant of science, history, literature, and other such genteel subjects.

But there was a much more serious defect in this handsome man, considered as a possible admirer. He was a widower, and a widower with incumbrances. He had a wife thirty years old in the graveyard, and he had two children of eight and ten who were not there. It was annoying to Olympia to see him help this boy and this girl to buttered slapjacks, and then bend upon herself a glance of undisguisable, tender appetite. Had he rolled in his carriage and resided in a mansion on Saltonstall Avenue, she might have been able to put up with his weeds and his paternity; but in a mere manufacturer of refrigerators, whose business was by no means colossal, these trappings of woe and pledges to society were little less than repulsive.

"I can never, never let him speak to me about it," said the young lady, with excitement, when her mother hinted to her that Mr. Vane seemed to be drifting toward an offer; "he is *so* common!"

"You must get married some time, I suppose," sighed Mrs. Smiles, whose pride had had a fall as splintering as that of Humpty Dumpty, and who found it hard work to support two stylish daughters. "Men who are not common are rare in our present circle."

"I would rather be an old maid than take a widower with two children," asserted Olympia.

"But how would the old maid live in case her mother should be removed?" asked the parent, pained in heart by her own plain-dealing, but feeling that it was called for.

The spinster who had never spun nor done any other remunerative labor could not answer this question. Presently it might have been observed that a tear was rolling down her cheek. Hard, hard indeed is the condition of a proud girl who sees herself encompassed by the thorny hedges of poverty, with no escape therefrom but a detested match, — a match as disagreeable to smell at as one of the brimstone species.

"Don't throw away this chance without fairly considering it," continued the widow. "Mr. Vane is a prosperous man, and a growing man every way. He has good manners, barring some slang phrases. He likes to talk about sensible subjects and to inform himself. Ten years hence you may find him your superior and have reason to be proud of him. A clever wife would help him forward wonderfully. He is a man that the right kind of a woman could make over and make fit for any circle."

MRS. SMILES was so

deeply interested in this subject that she talked much more firmly and impressively than was her wont.

Her manner, however, was pathetically mild and meek, as of a woman who is accustomed to be trampled upon by misfortune, and of a mother who has learned to bow down to her children.

She was a somewhat worn creature; originally, indeed, of fair outlines both physical and spiritual; but considerably rubbed out and defaced by the storms of adversity. She reminded one of those statues which travelers have seen in Italian court-yards, which were once, no doubt, rounded, vigorous, clean-cut, sparkling, and every way comely, but which, being made of too soft a marble, or beaten upon too long by winds and rains, have lost distinctness of lineament and brightness of color. "A good liquor at the start, but too much matured somehow'r nuther," judged one of her boarders, Mr. Jonas Damson, the grocer.

Yet this seemingly dilapidated and really tottering woman was the entire support, financially and morally, of two healthy daughters. Why? Because she was a relic of the time when ladies were not mere dandies; when work steadily done and responsibility loyally borne trained their characters into vigor; when they, like their men, were producers as well as consumers. Mrs. Smiles was not as highly educated as Olympia; she could not talk, whether wisely or foolishly, of so many subjects; but industrially and morally she was worth six of her.

Well, as this sorrowfully forethoughted mother had foreseen, the proposal of marriage came at last. John Vane popped the question with the terror and anguish and confusion natural to a self-made man who is madly in love with a "born lady." His tender heart, hysterical with affectionate fear and desire, nearly pounded the breath out of him while he uttered his message. What he said he was not then sanely conscious of, and could never afterwards distinctly remember. He may have spoken as beautiful words as lover ever did, or he may have expressed himself in the slang which Olympia found so repellent. But five minutes later he had forgotten the most momentous speech of his life; the particulars of it had departed from him as irretrievably as the breath in which they had been uttered; they were as completely gone as the odors of last year's flowers. Olympia's response, however, remained engraven upon his soul with sad distinctness; it was as plain as, "Sacred to the memory of," cut into the marble of a gravestone.

"Mr. Vane, I sincerely respect you, and I thank you for this mark of your esteem, but I cannot be your wife," was the decorous but unsympathetic form of service which she read over his hopes.

He essayed to implore, to argue his suit, to ask why, etc. But she would not hear him. "It cannot be," she interrupted, hastily and firmly; "I tell you, Mr. Vane, it cannot be."

And so, what seemed to him his ghost, went out from her presence, to walk the earth in cheerless unrest.

Of course, however, there was yet hope in the depths of his wretchedness, like a living though turbid spring of water in the bottom of a ruined well. He still wanted this girl; meant to bring her somehow to favor his suit; trusted in cheerful moments that she would yet be his. How should he move her? His friend, Mr. Jonas Damson, to whom he confided his venture and shipwreck, said to him, "John, you must show her your dignified side. Don't stay here and look melted butter at her, and cry in your coffee. Don't make a d—d fool of yourself, John, right under her nose. If you can't keep a good face on the business here, quit the house. Show her your independence. Let her see you can live without her. Sorry to lose you, John, from your old chair; but as a friend, I say, look up another hash house."

So, despite the plaintive reluctance of Mrs. Smiles, and despite his own desire to gaze daily upon his fair tormentor, the rejected lover changed residence. A rival boarding-house received John Vane and his two children, and his weekly payment of forty dollars. Next, after a little period of nerveless stupor, he rushed into the arena of politics. A politician of some local note, he was already able to send to the polls a "crowd" of the artisans whom he employed, or who knew him favorably as an old comrade in handicraft, and was consequently a sure candidate for the city council from his own ward, and a tolerably strong one for the State legislature.

Happily for his reawakened ambition, there had been a scandal of late among the "men inside politics." The member of Congress from the district of Slowburgh had been charged, and proved guilty too, of taking a one thousand dollar bribe from the "Gulf of Mexico and

Caribbean Sea Steam Navigation Company." Some old war-horses of the party, after vainly trying to hush the matter up, had decided to throw the Honorable James Bummer overboard.

"Bummer never could run again," they unanimously neighed and snorted. "To try to carry Jim Bummer would break down the organization. Jim must take a back seat, at least until this noise about him blows over, and give some fresh man a chance. A man, by George, that would cut the cherry-tree, and then tell of it, wasn't fit to guide the destinies of his country."

On the other hand, the personal friends of Bummer, that is to say, the men whom he had put into "soft places," or who had shared his "perks," supported him for many cogent reasons. They charged his enemies with encouraging the Copperheads and the Ku-Klux; with dishonoring American institutions in the face of monarchial Europe and of high Heaven, — both apparently hostile countries; worst of all, and what was insisted upon with the bitterest vehemence, they charged them with demoralizing the party, as if Bummer had moralized it. They denied the bribe doubly: first, they asserted that their man had accepted no stock in said Steam Navigation Company; second, they affirmed that he had as much right to own stock in it as any other citizen. They were stubborn and very uproariously wrathful, and not feeble in point of following. It was evident that the battle which must take place in the nominating caucus would be very fiercely contested. The friends of reform were forced to concede that, if they did not put up a candidate of admittedly high character and of great personal popularity, the meretricious veteran who now carried the banner of the district would continue to carry it. The whole momentous struggle, too, must center in the aforesaid caucus. Of course, after this mysterious agency had decided who should head the party, no good Republican could "go back on" the nominee, though he were the impenitent thief.

"John Vane, you must be there to-night," said Mr. Darius Dorman to our hero, a few hours previous to the caucus. "We may want you like the Devil," he added, without considering the precise uncomplimentary sense of the comparison.

Darius Dorman called himself a broker or general business man; he shaved notes when he had money, and when he had none speculated in city lots; he was always on the lookout for public jobs, such as paving contracts, and the supply of stores to the State militia; of late he was reported to be "engineering something through Congress." A very sooty and otherwise dirty chore this last must have been, if one might judge of it by the state of his linen, his hands, and even his face. Indeed, there was about Dorman such a noticeable and persistent tendency toward griminess, that it seemed as if he must be charged with some dark, pulverous substance, which shook through the interstices of his hide. Soap and water were apparently of no more use to him than they would be to a rag-baby of coarse calico stuffed with powdered charcoal instead of sawdust. His collar, his cuffs, his haggard, ghastly features, his lean, griping claws, his very fingernails, were always in a somber condition, verging in spots towards absolute smirch. This opaque finish of tint, coupled with a lean little figure and a lively, eager action, caused some persons to liken him to a scorched monkey. Other persons, whose imaginations had been solemnized by serious reading, could not look upon him without thinking of a goblin fresh from the lower regions, who had not found time since he came on

earth to wash himself thoroughly. In truth, if you ex-
amined his discoloration closely, you distinguished a tint
of ashes mingled with the coal smirch, so that a vivid
fancy might easily impute to him a subterranean origin
and a highly heated history. Another poetical supposi-
tion concerning him was, that his dusky maculations and
streakings were caused by the exudations of an exceedingly smutty soul. His age was unknown; no one in
Slowburgh knew when he was born, nor so much as
where he came from; but the iron-grey of his unkempt,
dusty hair suggested that he must be near fifty.

"They mean to put up Saltonstall against Bummer,
don't they?" asked John Vane, with a languid air, as if
he took little interest in the caucus.

"Yes, but it won't work," replied Dorman. "Saltonstall
is altogether too much of a gentleman to get the nomination. He's as calm and cold and dead as his buried
ancestors, the old governors. You can't get people to hurrah for a gravestone, even if it has a fine name on it. In
fact, the fine name is a disadvantage; American freemen
hate an aristocrat. It's really curious to see how Saltonstall's followers are killing him off. They are saying that,
because he is the son of an honorable, he ought to be
an honorable himself, and that he will do the right thing
for the sake of his forefathers. Our voters don't see it in
that light. They want plain people to become honorables.
Besides, who wants a Congressman to be fussy? The
chaps inside politics know that they won't get any favors
out of a man who has a high and mighty character to
nurse. I tell you that Saltonstall won't get the nomination. Bummer won't get it either. Some third man is
bound to come in; and you may be the very fellow. So,
don't fail to be on hand, Vane. Everything depends on
your showing yourself. When you are called for, rise

up to the full height of your manly figger, and see what a yell there'll be for Honest John Vane."

"O, pshaw! nonsense, now," smiled Vane, shaking his large and shapely head; but none the less he resolved to attend the caucus, and, indeed, positively promised to do so.

ALTHOUGH Darius

Dorman was noted for his unfulfilled prophecies, — for instance, frequently making business predictions which caused such widows and orphans as believed in him to lose their money, — he on this occasion hit the nail of the future pretty squarely on the head.

As soon as the caucus had been organized and had listened to a pair of brief speeches urging harmonious action, it split into two furiously hostile factions, each headed by one of the gentlemen who had talked harmony. Fierce philippics were delivered, some denouncing Bummer for being a taker of bribes and a pilferer of the United States Treasury, and some denouncing Saltonstall (as near as could be made out) for being a gentleman. So suspicious of each other's adroitness were the two parties, and so nearly balanced did they seem to be in numbers, that neither dared press the contest to a ballot. The war of by no means ambrosial words went on until the air of the hall became little less than mephitic, and the leading patriots present had got as hoarse and nearly as black in the face as so many crows. At last, when accommodation was clearly impossible, and the chiefs of the contending parties were pretty well fagged with their exertions, Darius Dorman sprang to his feet (if, indeed, they were not hoofs), and proposed the name of his favored candidate.

"I beg leave to point the way to a compromise which will save the party from disunion and from defeat," he screamed at the top of a voice penetrating enough to cleave Hell's thickest vapors. "As Congressman for this district, I nominate Honest John Vane."

Another broker and general contractor, whose prompt inspiration, by the way, had been previously cut and dried with great care, instantly and, as he said, spontaneously seconded the motion. Then, in rapid succession, a workingman who had learned the joiner's trade with Vane, and a Maine liquor law orator who had more than once addressed fellow-citizens in his teetotal company, made speeches in support of the nomination. The joiner spoke with a stammering tongue and a bewildered mind, which indicated that he had been put up for the occasion by others, and put up to it, too, without regard to any fitness except such as sprang from the fact of his being one of the "hard-handed sons of toil," — a class revered and loved to distraction by men whose business it is to "run the political machine." The practised orator palavered in a fluent, confident sing-song, as brassily penetrating as the tinkle of a bell, and as copious in repetitions. "Let the old Republican," he chanted, "come out for him; let the young Republican come out for him; let the Democrat, yea, the very Democrat, come out for him; let the native-born citizen come out for him; let the foreign-born citizen come out for him; let the Irishman, and the German, and the colored man come out for him; let the cold-water temperance man come out for him; let the poor, tremulous, whiskey-rotted debauchee come out for him; let the true American of every sort and species

come out for him; let *all*, yea, *all* men come out for awn-
est Jawn Vane!"

There was no resisting such appeals, coming as they
did from the "masses." The veteran leaders in politics
saw that the "cattle," as they called the common herd of
voters, were determined for once to run the party char-
iot, and most of them not only got out of the way, but
jumped up behind. They were the first to call on Vane
to show himself, and the first to salute his rising with
deafening applause, and the last to come to order. A
vote was taken on his nomination, and the ayes had it
by a clear majority.

Then Darius Dorman proposed, for the sake of party
union, for the sake of the good old cause, for the sake
of this great Republic, to have the job done over by
acclamation. There was not an audible dissenting voice;
on the contrary, there was "wild enthusiasm." The old
war-horses and wheel-horses and leaders all fell into the
traces at once, and neighed and snorted and hurrahed
until their hard foreheads dripped with patriotic perspir-
ation, every drop of which they meant should be paid
for in municipal or State or Federal dollars.

Many elders of the people escorted Vane home that
evening, and sat up with him with a devotion which
deserved no end of postmasterships. Of all these admirers, however, the one who snuggled closest and stayed
latest, was that man of general business, Darius Dorman.

"John, a word with you," he began confidentially, after
his rivals had all departed, at the same time drawing
close up to Vane's side, and insinuating a dark, horny
claw into one of his buttonholes; "I think you must own,
John, that I have done more than any other man to help
you into this soft thing. Would you mind hearing a word
of advice?"

"Go on," replied Vane, with that cheery, genial smile which had done so much toward making him popular; "I owe you an oyster supper."

"You'll owe me a good many, if you follow my counsel," continued Dorman. "Now listen to me. You'll be elected; that's a sure thing. But after that, what? Why, you've got a great career open to you, and you may succeed in it, or you may fail. It all depends on what branch of politics you work at. Don't go into the war memories and the nigger worshiping; all those sentimental dodges are played out. Go into finance. The great national questions to be attended to now are the questions of finance. Spread yourself on the tariff, the treasury, the ways and means, internal improvements, subsidy bills, and relief bills. Dive into those things, and stick there. It's the only way to cut a figure in politics and to make politics worth your while."

"I've thought of that already," replied Vane hopefully. "It's my line, you know, — business, money-matters, practical finance."

"Exactly!" assented Dorman. "Well, throw yourself on it, especially internal improvements and subsidy bills, — that sort of thing. When you get in, I shall have a scheme to propose to you which you'll like to push. Something big, something national, something on a grand scale. If it goes through, it will make reputations, and fortunes, too, for that matter," he added, with a glance at Vane which was monkey-like in its sly greediness.

"I don't propose to go into Congress for money," answered Honest John Vane.

"O, of course not!" leered Dorman. "You want honor, and the respect of the country, and so on. Well, this is just the kind of a measure that will fix the eyes of the country on whoever carries it through. You'll be delighted with it, I know you will. However, I mustn't blow it now; the time hasn't come. All I meant to say was, that I wanted you to keep a hand ready for it when it comes around. Well, that's all. I congratulate you, I do, with all my heart. Good-night."

Next day all Slowburgh was talking of Vane's unexpected nomination for Congress. "Queer choice," said some people. "Everything happens in politics. Vane is as ignorant of real public business as he is of Sanscrit." Others remarked, "Well, we shall have a decent man in the place. John is a good-hearted, steady, honest fellow. Not very brilliant, but he will learn the ropes as others have; and then he is so confounded honest!"

After a nomination, as we Americans know by wearisome experience, there must be an election. The struggle between the two great and noble parties of the ins and the outs which divided Slowburgh was on this occasion unusually vehement. The opposition, trusting to the divisions which they supposed to exist in the administration ranks, made such a fight as despair makes when it changes to hope.

Many of those genteel and highly cultivated persons who ordinarily hate politics became excited; and among these abnormally agitated ones was Miss Olympia Smiles. It seems very strange, and yet it was natural. Discovering that her rejected suitor had become an object of interest to all Slowburgh, she also, by mere human infection or contagion, began to find him interesting. We know how women go on when they once begin; we remember how, during the war, they flung their smiles, their trinkets, and seemingly their hearts, to unintroduced volunteers; we have all seen them absorb enthusiasm from those around, and exhale it with doubled heat. So it went, during that political crisis, with the young lady in question. Before the campaign had roared half-way through its course, she was passionately interested in it, and electioneered for her preferred candidate even to her mother's Democratic boarders.

"Measures are of little consequence," she declared when she was argued with and confuted by these prejudiced individuals. "What we want and all that we want is good men in high places. And, if I had a vote," she frequently asserted with a convincing blush, so beautiful was it, — "if I had a vote, it should go for Honest John Vane."

Honest John heard of this and of other similar speeches of Olympia's, and they seemed to him altogether the most eloquent efforts of the campaign. They gave him a joy which a connoisseur in happiness might envy, — a joy which more than once, when he was alone, brought the tears into his eyes. He had cherished no spite against the girl because she had refused him; and he did not now say to himself scornfully that she would like to be the wife of a Congressman, but that it was too late; he was too thoroughly a good fellow and true lover to secrete any such venom of thought or feeling. The hope that he might yet win Olympia Smiles, and devote to her such part of his life as his country and the refrigerator business could spare, opened to him the prospect of a little heaven upon earth. Meeting her one day in the street, he ventured to stop her, thanked her stammeringly for her favorable wishes, pressed her hand with unconscious vehemence, and parted from her with a swimming head.

Olympia was sensible enough and sensitive enough to carry away a rejoiced heart from this interview. She knew now that she could still have this hero of the hour, and she began to find that she wanted him, at least a little. He was no longer common and, metaphorically speaking, unclean in her patrician eyes. She looked after his tall, robust figure as it went from her, and thought how manly and dignified and even handsome it was. His condition of widowerhood became vague to her mind; the gravestone of his wife vanished like a ghost overtaken by daybreak; even his two cherished children could not cast a shadow over her feelings. It would surely be something fine to enter the capital of the nation as the wife of one of the nation's law-givers; it would at least be far better than growing into old-maidenhood amid the sordid anxieties of a boarding-house. Aristocratic as her breed was, and delicate as had been her culture, the title of Mrs. John Vane tempted her. Should she throw a net for this man, drag him back to her feet, and accept him? Well, perhaps so; but first she would see whether he carried his election; she must not be caught by a mere prophecy of greatness and glory.

Let us not be severe upon the young lady because of her prudence, asserting that she carried it to the point of calculating selfishness. As far as concerned love-making, this was her first essay in that deliberate virtue; and impartial psychology will not express angry surprise at her over-doing it a little, so much is the human mind ruled by the law of undulation or pulsation, or, in other words, so apt is it to go from one extreme to another. Besides, in a matter so permanently serious to woman as marriage, it is pardonable and even praiseworthy that she should be cautious.

WELL, Honest John Vane triumphed at the polls, and became member of Congress for the district of Slowburgh.

Let us glance now at his qualifications for the splendid and responsible position of which his fellow-citizens had pronounced him worthy.

He was, to use a poetical figure, in the flower of his age, or, to use a corresponding arithmetical figure, about thirty-five.

He had, as he and his admirers supposed, fully formed his character, and settled it on a stable platform of worthy habits and creeds.

He was commercially honest, indefatigably industrious, a believer in the equal rights of man, a strenuous advocate of the Maine liquor law, a member, if I am not greatly mistaken, of the church, and every way in good repute among grave, conscientious people.

His "war record" was admitted to be unimpeachable; that is to say, he had consistently and unflinchingly denounced the Rebellion "from its inception"; if he had not fought for the Union on the battle-field, he had fought for it on the stump and in the chimney-corner.

In all his geographical sentiments he was truly American, even to occasional misunderstanding of our foreign affairs, and to the verge of what one might call safe rashness.

He wanted somebody (meaning of course somebody else) to thrash England well for the Trent affair, and to annihilate her for the Alabama outrages. He affirmed in one of his public "efforts" that our claim for indirect damages should be prosecuted, if necessary, "before the court of high Heaven," which phrase he always regarded as one of his happiest inspirations, although he had found it "in the paper."

He contended that it was our mission, and consequently our duty to interfere in behalf of oppressed Cuba by bringing it within the pale of our own national debt, and generally to extend the area of freedom over such countries as would furnish us with a good market for our home productions, and a mild climate for our invalids.

At the same time he did not want to go to war for these benevolent purposes; for war, as he frequently remarked, was a frightful thing, and we had already shed blood enough to show that we would fight rather than submit to outrage; he only proposed that we "should sit still in our grandeur and let those fellows gravitate toward us."

His views concerning internal affairs were marked by an equal breadth and thickness. He held that the industry of the American producer should be protected, at no matter what cost to the American consumer.

He was opposed to the introduction of Chinese cheap labor as being injurious to the "noble class of native artisans," however it might benefit our equally noble farmers by furnishing them with low-priced tools, shoes, and clothing.

He believed that our system of government was the purest and most economical in the world, when it was not abused by municipal rings, public defaulters, railroad legislation, and lobbyists of the State and national capitals.

He argued that rotation in office is republican, because it "gives every citizen a fair chance"; and that it is a means of national education, because it tempts even the dregs of society to aspire to responsibility and power.

In the whole superficies of our civil affairs he saw but one error which needed serious and instant attention, namely, the franking privilege. If that could be removed, and two millions thereby saved annually out of a budget of three or four hundred millions, he thought that the legislative sun of American democracy would be left without a spot, the exemplar and despair of other tax-laden nations.

Such was the optimist and amiable patriotism of Congressman Vane. While we cannot but admire it from a sentimental point of view, we are obliged to regret that it did not rise from a wider base of information. Whether the conclusions of this self-taught statesman were right or wrong, they were alike the offspring of ignorance, or at best of half knowledge. We can only palliate his dark-mindedness with regard to American politics on the ground that it was cosmically impartial, and extended to the politics of all other countries, ancient and modern.

He had never heard that our civil institutions were not exclusively our own invention, but germinated naturally from the colonial charters granted by "tyrannical Britain." He believed that, because Queen Victoria cost England half as much annually as Boss Tweed cost the single city of New York, therefore England ought to be and must be on the verge of a revolution. He supposed that Prussia must be an unlettered and dishonestly governed country, because it is ruled by a king. Of the ancient states of Greece he had a general idea that they were republics, with some form or other of representative government, Sparta being as much a democracy as Athens. It would have been news to him, as fresh as anything arriving by telegraph, that Attica was legislated for by a single municipality, and that its inhabitants were three-fourths slaves. The Rome of his mind was also a representative democracy, and its conscript fathers were, perhaps, selected by conscription, like recruits for some armies. Of the tyranny of capitalists and of the corruption of magistrates and tax-collectors in that most famous of all republics, he was as ignorant as he was, or strove to be, of similar phenomena in the United States. His reading in ancient history began and ended with Rollin, to the exclusion of Niebuhr, Arnold, Grote, Curtius, and Mommsen, of whom, indeed, he had never heard. It may be thought that, for the sake of a joke, I am exaggerating Mr. Vane's Eden-like nakedness and innocence; but I do solemnly and sadly assure the reader that I have not robbed him of a single fig-leaf of knowledge which belonged to him.

As for political economy, he had never seen a line of Adam Smith, Mill, Bastiat, or any of their fellows; they not being quoted in "the papers" which furnished his sole instruction in statesmanship, and almost his sole literary entertainment. He was too completely unaware of these writers and of their conclusions to attack them with the epithet of theorists or of *doctrinaires*. All that he knew of political economy was that Henry C. Carey had written some dull letters about it to the Tribune, and that the Pennsylvania iron-men considered him "an authority to tie to." His vague impression was that the science advocated the protection of native manufactures, and that consequently it would be worth looking into whenever he found a moment's respite from business and politics.

Certainly, it was wonderful how little this self-taught soul could see into a millstone, even when it was his own and he ground at it daily. He was a manufacturer of refrigerators; and very thankful indeed was he that Congress had imposed high import duties on foreign specimens of that "line of goods"; it was patriotic and wise, he thought, thus to protect American industry against the pauper labor of Europe. Meantime, he did not consider that his zinc and hinges, and screws and nails, and paint and varnish were taxed; that his own food, raiment, fuel, and shelter, and also the food, raiment, fuel, and shelter of his workmen, were likewise taxed; that, in short, taxation increased the expense of all the materials of labor and the necessaries of life which made up the principal cost of his fabrics; and that it was mainly because of these things that he was unable to produce refrigerators at anything like the ante-tax prices.

The government put a little money into one of his pockets and took the same sum or more out of several others; and he was so far from seeing that the legerdemain did not help him, or perhaps hurt him, that he enthusiastically sang praises to it. There had been a time when he exported, when he could boast that a portion of his revenue came from beyond sea, when he had hopes of building up a fine market abroad. Not so now;

foreigners could no longer afford to buy of him; they made all their own refrigerators. John Vane did not comprehend this adverse providence any more than if he had himself been made of pine and lined with zinc. He compendiously remarked, "Our prices rule too high for those beggars," and was patriotically proud of the fact, though sadly out of pocket by it. Such was his insight into legislation where it directly concerned his own bread and butter. You can imagine what a clear view he had of those labyrinths of it which ramify through the general body politic.

But if he was not an instructed soul, he was at all events an honest one. That attribute all his fellow-citizens conceded to him, even those who did not see the wisdom or beauty of it; it was a matter of common fame in Slowburgh, and, one might almost say, of common conversation. Men who could not get trusted for five dollars spoke of him approvingly as "Honest John Vane," feeling, perhaps, that in so doing they imputed to themselves a little of his righteousness, so illogical are the mental processes of sinners.

It is worth while to relate (if only to encourage our youth in the ways of virtue) how easily he had acquired this high repute. While a member of the State legislature he had refused a small bribe from a lobbyist, and had publicly denounced the briber. That this inexpensive outburst of probity should secure him widespread and permanent fame does not, to be sure, shed a very pleasing light over the character which is borne by our law-givers. But we will not enter upon that subject; it perhaps needs more whitewash than we possess. We will simply call the attention of Sunday school pupils and Young Men's Christian Associations to the cheering fact

that, at a prime cost of one hundred dollars, our towns-
man was able to arise and shine upon a people noted
for its political purity as "Honest John Vane!" Only one
hundred in greenbacks (about ninety in gold) out of
pocket, and the days of Washington come again! I should
suppose that, for say twice the figure, a legislator of the
period might get the title of "Father of his Country."

SUCH as we have described was John Vane's slender outfit for the labors and responsibilities of a Congressman at the time he became one.

Was it sufficient? Slowburgh, taken collectively, thought it was. He was too ignorant to be a professor in the State university, or even a teacher in one of the city schools; but it was presumed that he would answer well enough as a law-giver for a complicated Republic containing forty millions of people.

The great majority of his constituents did not suppose that their representative needed any more intelligence or moral stamina than would just enable him to find out what were the "party measures," and faithfully to vote for them. The few who believed that he ought to be acquainted either with finance, or political economy, or constitutional limitations, or international law, and that furthermore he should be a person of tried character and honor, — these few eccentrics had no political influence. Such were the happy-go-lucky credences at which universal suffrage had arrived in this exceptional district of Slowburgh.

But as this state of public opinion was not John Vane's work, we must neither blame him nor praise him for it.

We ought even to take a respectful and compassionate interest in him, as a good-hearted man of fair repute who was about to be severely tried by temptation, and who, even in his hour of triumph, had his pathetic hopes and fears. It is creditable to his sentimental nature that, amid all the visions of greatness which naturally flocked about him, he did not forget his love for the daughter of the boarding-house keeper, but rather remembered her the more tenderly because he had a sort of throne to share with her. When he heard that he was elected, his first desire was to seek her presence and offer himself once more. In this mind he faithfully remained; but how should he transform it into deed? Having been refused by her, and having departed from her mother's house, really in humble sorrow, but seemingly in lofty dudgeon, he simply supposed that he must not call upon her.

Should he write? Well, it is very strange to tell, but nevertheless it is solemnly true, that this Congressman elect distrusted his ability to compose a suitable epistle for the occasion. Of course he could spell correctly, and, as for business letters, he wrote a dozen or so a day, and very good ones too. A speech also he could make, for nature had given him that commonplace fluency of utterance which does so much duty in our public affairs, and he had acquired confidence in delivery by practice in caucuses, debating-clubs, and, if I do not err, in prayer-meetings. But in English composition of the elegant and delicate sort, he was entirely inexperienced. He said to himself that, if he should write a declaratory note to Miss Smiles, something common, something lacking in high breeding, might creep into it, which would be sure to disgust this genteel and highly educated young lady, and cause her, as he stated it in his anxious mind, "to put another veto on him." So, for several days, our states-man elect walked the streets of the city which had de-lighted to honor him, with a prevalently humble and troubled spirit.

Accident at last favored him; or, perhaps, it may have been a stroke of feminine providence; for women do sometimes condescend to order their own destinies. Once again Olympia Smiles met him on the street, and most graciously allowed herself to be stopped by him, if, in-deed, she did not herself do the stopping. Vane was for a moment dumb, for he remembered that he had nothing special to say to her except that he adored her, and it did not seem to him quite proper to interview her just there on that subject. Olympia came to his rescue with that quickness of mind which young ladies rarely lose and that mercy which they sometimes have.

"Mr. Vane, I am glad to meet you," she smiled. It was a very cordial speech surely, but it did not at all diminish her maidenly dignity, so well did she know how to rule her manner. "I have really longed to con-gratulate you on your victory," she continued. "It gives me a great deal of pleasure."

"I thank you exceedingly," stammered John, blushing with unspeakable joy and fright. "I heard you were good enough to take my side during the campaign. I was very much obliged to you for it, I am sure."

He showed no anger and he put on no dignity, though he seemed to hear even then her humiliating words, "It can never be." In the matter of loving, he was surely a model soul, and, so far as that goes, well worth any woman's winning.

"Why don't you come and see us?" she resumed, after a moment of natural hesitation over the entangling query.

"I had hoped that we should always remain good friends."

She looked uncommonly attractive as she uttered this, for there was an enchantment about her beyond that of mere beauty. Her agitation not only filled her cheeks with color, and her eyes with tremulous light, but drew from her whole being a mysterious influence which we might, perhaps, call a halo of enticement. She longed so earnestly to bring her discarded lover back to her feet, that he could not but be vaguely aware of the longing.

"I shall be delighted to call," replied John Vane, so much moved that he could not devise a fine speech, but delivering himself with the simplicity of high breeding. "Will you allow me to see you this evening?"

"Yes," murmured Olympia, drawing her breath with some difficulty. "Do come."

Then, unwilling to say more for fear of exposing her feelings too clearly, she gave him a bewildering smile and went her way. Her superb figure thrilled in every vein with excitement, and she could hardly set her little bootees upon the ground steadily. Citizen John Vane had had no attractions for her; but she could not help being drawn by the member of Congress. After the fashion of women, she instinctively admired a man who rules his fellow-men, and causes them to do him reverence. As he, like all masculine flesh, adored beauty and delicacy, so she, like all feminine flesh, worshiped strength and authority.

That evening John called, in his best suit, at his old boarding-house, and was received there with a warmth which melted the icy past out of his mind. Mrs. Smiles, who had always liked him, and who had been sentimentally pained as well as financially injured by losing him from her table, called up all her social graces of bygone fashionable days to do him honor. Julia Maria, Olympia's younger sister, only nineteen years old at the time, saluted him in her pert but alluring way as "the delegation from Slowburgh." Olympia herself, that experienced though not hardened veteran of the world, robed herself in just the right mixture of cordiality and dignity. Both in a moral and in a wardrobe sense, she had taken great pains to get herself up for the occasion. She was arrayed in her best garnet silk; and we ought to add the statement that it was her only really good and fresh one, — a pathetic circumstance in view of the fact that she dearly loved gorgeous apparel, and that it suited her style of beauty. The rich and noble color of the garnet lent additional splendor to the flush on her brunette cheeks, and to the liquid sparkle of her dark eyes. There was an emerald cross (a relic of her mother's former prosperity) on her breast; and several rings, of like moving history, sent out little glimmers of gentility from her fingers. The fine raiment and the authentic splendor of the jewels became her, and made her more queenly, more like a Cleopatra, than even her wont. John Vane had never before seen her so beautiful, and he was dazzled to that degree that he forgot his own political majesty, and sat before her on the edge of a chair, a most humble Antony.

"I am truly rejoiced at your success, Mr. Vane," chanted the mother, who felt it her duty to open the way toward full cordiality.

"We shall now have an honest man to represent us," she continued, repeating such political talk as she had fully caught the sense of while serving her boarders. "And a man of ability, too," she quickly added, vaguely conscious that an imputation of honesty alone is small praise. "Knowing what you have done in life hitherto, I feel sure that you will be very useful in your new sphere."

"Do manage, Mr. Vane, to have a gay season in Washington," put in Julia Maria; "and then do get me an invite to spend the winter there."

Olympia lost a little of her air of repose, and glanced uneasily at her sister. Was it within the range of possibility that this young chit should skip into the arena and carry off the prize by dint of mere girlish forwardness and flippancy? Mrs. Smiles also saw the peril, and, in obedience to the eye of her eldest, sweetly sent Julia Maria down stairs with a message to the cook.

"I don't know what sort of a figger I shall cut in Congress," observed John Vane, modestly. "But you may be sure, Mrs. Smiles, that I shall do my honest best. I hope sincerely that I shall merit the compliments you are so polite as to pay me."

"O, *indeed* you will!" broke in both mother and daughter, eagerly.

"And yet, I should think you would tremble at the thought of assuming *such* responsibilities," continued Mrs. Smiles, gazing with real veneration at her once favored boarder, now the choice of the people. "It must be such a terrible thing to decide on the President's salary, and such-like important questions."

"O, that's very simple!" answered the Congressman elect, pardonably anxious to show a little bit of his political lore. "You see, the President's salary is fixed by law, and there's no discussion over it."

"Yes, but you may have to vote on the law," pursued the good lady, eager to make up some work for her hero.

"O, as to that," stammered Vane, who had been drawn beyond his depth, "I dare say that may come up sometimes! Of course, when it does, Congress attends to it."

"Certainly," chimed in Mrs. Smiles, delighted that it should be so, because it enhanced her friend's glory. "I remember hearing Mr. Smiles, my poor husband, — this was when we were in better circumstances, Mr. Vane, — I remember hearing him say that Congress is only too powerful. He took a great interest in politics, Mr. Smiles did. It is the business of a statesman, he used to say. Often and often I've heard him say it."

By this time Olympia was glancing sidelong at her mother, as she had previously glanced at her sister. Mrs. Smiles noted the look and divined from it that she was in the girl's way, and proceeded to remove herself.

"Dear me! I wonder if Julia gave my message," she

exclaimed, in a simulated tone of reminiscence. "Do excuse me for a few moments, Mr. Vane. You know a housekeeper has her affairs."

"Certainly, Mrs. Smiles," bowed John, who was rejoiced to have her depart, although he also felt nervous.

As soon as the two "young people" were left alone, Olympia rose from the chair where she had been sitting in isolated dignity, advanced to our Congressman with an air of cordial interest, and placed herself by his side on a sofa.

"Now tell me *all* about it," she murmured with a bewildering smile. "I have so *longed* to question you! I wanted to give you some intelligent sympathy. Tell me *all* your plans of legislation, as far as it is proper to tell them to a woman."

Such a gush from such a source was intoxicating to the heart, and furthermore it was inspiring to the mind. Some thousands of psychologists have already remarked that a man can always talk easily, if you will let him talk about himself and provide him with an interested and interesting listener. John Vane at once lost his embarrassment and found that this was indeed a land of free speech. He had a fluent utterance, as we have already indicated, and on this occasion he beat his best time on the platform. He told all that he knew about national politics, and some things which neither he nor any other man ever knew.

"O, that will be noble work!" exclaimed Olympia, when he had fully exposed his plan for renovating and purifying the Republic by rescinding the franking privilege. "We shall all owe you a vast debt of gratitude," she continued, without in the least comprehending how the reform would benefit her or any other human creature.

"But do you think it possible to eradicate such an estab-lished and wide-spread *abuse*?" she continued, calling it what he had called it, and thereby causing him to marvel at her discrimination. "Here are all these greedy people all over the country, crazy to get these big books and reports that you speak of. How do you think they will bear being deprived of them? Of course they will be-come your bitter enemies. Don't you think it would be safer, and better in the long run, to begin with some easier work, where there would not be millions to op-pose you? Of course I am dreadfully ignorant of these political matters," she naïvely confessed, discovering by his face that she had made some blunder, which she certainly had as to the millions. "You must forgive me for venturing suggestions. I ought not to try to discuss matters so much above me. But I am eager to have you succeed from the very start! *O, so eager!*" she added, rolling up her fine eyes enthusiastically.

"O Miss Smiles! I do heartily thank you for your interest," gasped John Vane, barely restraining himself from falling on his majestic knees.

At this moment the impertinent cheap parlor clock struck ten. Congressman Vane started and stared at its round face with astonishment. Since Mrs. Smiles had left the room "for a few moments," more than an hour had elapsed.

"I must be going," he observed, remembering an ap-pointment, at ten precisely, with certain leading mana-gers of politics.

"O, it is not late!" pleaded Olympia. "I have but just begun to get interested — I mean, to understand these matters."

But the Congressman felt that it would not do to let

his potent allies wait long, and, humbly pleading his appointment, he persisted in rising.

"Do call again soon," urged the young lady. "I want to show you that I am still your friend, — one of your most *sincere* friends," she added fervently, giving him her hand.

John Vane could not resist the temptation; he impulsively pressed that hand to his lips. "You know how I feel!" he gasped in apology, and then in haste made his dizzy way to the door.

"O, how could you!" whispered Olympia in feigned remonstrance. But her cheek was red with pride and pleasure, and her parting glance was of a nature to fill him with hope.

A sense of justice compels us to state that this young lady was not merely a clever hypocrite, cold-heartedly planning for herself a prosperous marriage. During the two months in which John Vane had fought his election fight and won his really brilliant victory, she had not only lost all her early disdain of him, but had gradually learned to admire him, to wish to win him, and to like him. People are often loved, not merely for what they are themselves, but also for their adventitious surroundings. I myself feel that I might have a passion for a tolerably plain queen, if her Majesty should distinctly and magnificently encourage me. Just in this natural, and therefore, I suppose, rational and proper manner, Olympia "fancied" and in a certain sense loved Mr. Vane because he was a Congressman and a celebrity.

A learned pig, or any other intellect of a second-rate order, might predict with accuracy the result of such a state of things. These two people, who so earnestly wanted each other, soon managed to have each other.

But, although John Vane made an easy conquest, it was none the less an unexpected one to him, and a matter of great and keen joy. When he at last dared to say to Olympia, "Will you be my wife?" and when she leaned with downcast eyes toward him and whispered, "I will," he was as much astonished with gladness as if he had been received bodily into heaven. Just in that moment his feelings, and we may hopefully venture to add hers also, were as admirable and enviable as the emotions of the most select and highly educated natures would average under the same circumstances, and might easily be accepted as the sure harbingers of a happy married life.

We shall see in the sequel, when Mr. and Mrs. Vane come to be exposed to the temptations of Washington, whether these seraphic visitants prophesied correctly.

7

IN due time John Vane took his lovely bride to the national capital, and entered upon his triple career as a social magnate, a lawgiver, and a reformer.

He was a bloomingly happy man at the period of that advent, and he could surely allege satisfactory reasons for his beatitude. He had attained eminence early in life; there were few younger Congressmen than himself. His fame as an incorruptible soul had preceded him; and because of it he had been received by his brother legislators with a deference which spoke well for them: as if they also were honest or admired probity theoretically, or at the very least bowed to popular prejudice on the subject. He had, as he supposed, a sure entry into the hitherto unvisited region which he called high society, and by his side walked a being who seemed to him perfectly fitted to guide him among those Delectable Mountains. Finally, his wife was the object of his robust, undivided affection, and, to the best of his knowledge and belief, returned it with interest.

But, however pure and abundant may be the sources of earthly joy, some turbid stream will ever and anon rile them, bubbling up no doubt from the infernal regions. Before long Vane discovered, or rather had it borne in upon him, that Olympia was not pleased with her architectural surroundings, nor with their upholstery attributes. His apartments, it must be conceded, were not fine; they were just that kind of tarnished, frowsy lodgings which Congressmen of moderate means grumble at, but perforce put up with; such lodgings as one is sure to find abundantly in any city which is crowded during one half of the year and deserted during the other half. Even Vane, whose self-made career had not left him a sybarite, was obliged to admit that the bedroom smelt unpleasantly of a neighboring stable, and that the parlor was dingy and scantily furnished.

"O, this shabby Washington!" Olympia soon began to sigh. "What mean, musty, vile rooms! I don't see how we came to take them. I'm sure nobody but poorhouse people will visit us twice *here*."

"But, my dear petsy posy, what can be done?" gently replied John. "They are the best we could find at the figger, and the figger is as high as my pocket-book measures. Just look at the whole thing now," he continued, patiently recommencing an argument which he had already been driven to state more than once. "I'll show you exactly how I stand. As a source of income the refrigerator business don't count at present. I had to take in a partner to carry on the shop; and whether there'll be any profits or not I can't yet say. It won't be safe, at least not for the first year, to estimate my receipts at anything more than my Congressional salary. What I have to live on, then, is just five thousand dollars, and no more."

"But that is a great deal," interrupted Olympia, who had never had anything whatever to do with the boarding-house responsibilities, and was consequently as ignorant of the cost of living as Queen Victoria, and probably a great deal more so.

"Well, that depends on the rate of outgo," smiled the husband, hoping vainly to render his logic palatable by sugaring it with meekness. "Now, what are our expenses? First, there are the two children. I wanted to make things easy for your mother, and so I put their board at twenty-four dollars per week, which, with other bills, such as clothing, schooling, doctoring, etc., will foot up to eighteen hundred a year. It's awful, but I wanted to make it light on the old lady."

He smiled again, not noting how this reference to the maternal poverty jarred on Olympia.

"Then our board and rooms here," he continued, "cost forty dollars a week, and won't fall greatly below that while we are in Slowburgh, besides which you want a trip to Saratoga. So there goes another payment of two thousand and eighty dollars. That makes three thousand eight hundred and eighty, you see. All we have left for everything else — wardrobe, washing, servants, street-cars, hack-hire, and sundries — is only eleven hundred and twenty dollars. Can we fetch the twelve months round on that? I don't know yet. But I'm sure, we ought to wait and see, before we branch out any wider. Just look at it, my dear petsy posy, for yourself."

"I hate arithmetic," was the answer which dear petsy posy accorded to this painstaking exposition of weighty facts; "I always did hate it and always shall."

There are some persons so constituted that they will get furious with a thermometer for proving that a room is warm after they have pronounced it cold. Olympia, who already felt discontented with her husband for bringing her into these commonplace rooms, was little less than angry at him because his arguments in favor of retaining them were unanswerable. She did not care one straw for his reasons, except to hate them for controverting her wishes.

"I did think that I should be allowed to live in some style while I was in Washington," she continued to pout. "This kind of thing," with a disdainful glance at her furnishings, "I suppose I can bear it, if I must; but I do say that it is a very great disappointment to me."

Having been married before, John Vane was not much astonished at this persistence, but he could not help being grieved by it. It did seem to him rather hard that a wife whom he had taken out of the enforced frugality of a boarding-house should be just as eager for grandeur and as hostile to saving as if she had been reared in the lap of luxury and had brought him a fortune. Furthermore, a sad doubt, which has dolorously surprised many a husband beside him, now sprang upon him for the first time. "Is it possible," he asked himself, "that she is not going to be satisfied with succeeding through *my* success, but means to make her own glory the centre of our life?"

The first Mrs. Vane, whatever her shortcomings in other respects, had been content with such an abode as he could pay for, and had taken a pride in his growing business. But here was a new style of helpmeet; a helpmeet who apparently did not propose to live for him; who, on the contrary, intended that he should live for her, and that without regard to balancing his bank account. She had got a Congressman; but that almost continental fact did not satisfy her: she must have her own separate empire and glory. In short, Vane began dimly to suspect (although he did not at all know how to phrase the matter to himself) that he had married a "girl of the period," that fairest and greediest of all vampires. Being love-bewitched, however, he did not really believe in his calamity, and much less burst forth in wrath or lamentation.

"Well, my dear, we'll see about it," he said, cheeringly. "We'll keep our eyes open for some better shanty than this, and if the dollars seem plenty we'll pop into it."

This conditional promise of finer surroundings Olympia tacitly accepted as a positive agreement to provide the same, and went out that very day in search of first-class apartments, returning much annoyed at finding none vacant. To soothe her disappointment she got fifty dollars from her husband, purchased such damask curtains as could be had therefor, and so embellished her parlor. Vane winced a little; as a business man he saw that this was a poor way to prepare for getting into better lodgings; as a business man also he hated to spend money in lending attractions to another person's property. But he tried to persuade himself that he had got off tolerably cheap, and that his wife would learn economy and self-control in the course of time. Then, like many another Congressman who cannot rule his own expenditures, he turned his attention to reforming those of the nation.

The first thing to be done was to get in his bill for the abolition of the franking privilege. He had written it out months ago, and touched it up ever so many times since. After pulling aside those damask curtains in order to give himself some light, he took his well-scratched manuscript out of his trunk, and read it to himself aloud. As is frequently the case with persons little accustomed to composition, the sound of his own periods was agreeable to him, and the sense impressive, not to say sublime. It seemed to him that it was a good bill; that it was, all over its face and down its back, an honest man's bill; that every respectable fellow in the House would *have* to vote for it. He decided to make a clean copy of it just as it was, without another syllable of useless alteration. He had just squared himself and spread out his legs and put his head on one side for this "chore," and was in the very act of flourishing his right hand over the foolscap preparatory to executing a fine opening capital, when he was arrested by a ring at his door-bell. Presently in stamped his old acquaintance and most adroit wire-puller, Mr. Darius Dorman, followed by a stranger.

NO miracle having of late been performed for the benefit of Dorman (who, indeed, may have been altogether beyond the pale of heavenly interferences), he was as ungraciously fashioned and as disagreeably discolored as ever.

Earthly soap and water, it seemed, could not wash away that suspicious smear of charcoal and ashes which constituted his complexion, or which, perhaps, only hid its real tint.

Blurred, blotched, smoke-dried, wilted, uneasy, and agile, he looked and acted, as he had always looked and acted, to mortal eyes, like either a singed monkey or a bleached goblin, who had some unquenched sparks on his hide that would not let him be quiet.

To this brownie in bad preservation the person who accompanied him offered a pleasing contrast. He was a man of near seventy, but still slender in build and of an upright carriage; his face was long, venerably wrinkled, firm in expression, and yet unctuous with mildness and benevolence; his hair was long, straight, thin, and of a gray which verged on the reverend gloss of pure whiteness; his whole air was marked by a curious staidness and circumspectness which seemed to promise ascetic virtue. One would have said that here was a soul which had dwelt long on the pillar of self-sacrifice. If there was a certain sharpness amounting almost to cunning in the half-shut, faded, cold gray eyes, it might have been acquired, of course, by wary spying into the ambushes of this wicked world, and be only a proof of that serpent-like wisdom which goes properly with the harmlessness of the dove. If there was a show of grip about the close-shut mouth, as though it could hang on to an advantage like a mastiff to a bone, perhaps it might have resulted from a dogged struggle to hold fast to the right. On the whole, this gentleman's appearance was well calculated to inspire instant and entire confidence, providing the beholder were disposed by education to put faith in exteriors of the Puritanized cast.

"How are you, Vane?" exclaimed Dorman, cordially extending one of those hands which had such an air of having been rubbed in a fireplace. "Glad to see you at last where you belong; glad to see one right man in the right place. Let me make you acquainted with the Honorable Mr. Sharp, one of the leading members from the good old Whetstone State," he explained referring to a well-known Commonwealth. "Of course you have heard of Mr. Simon Sharp, the great financier and practical statesman. Mr. Sharp, this is Honest John Vane, the workingman's man, the plain people's man. By Beelzebub!" he added (for he had very odd fashions of swearing), "I'm glad to bring you two gentlemen together. You both travel the honest track. You'll make a team."

Mr. Vane and Mr. Sharp shook hands respectfully, and said what pleasant things they could think of. Our member noted with some surprise that his famous and puissant visitor had a singularly soft, ingratiating, obsequious,

116

nay, even sycophantic utterance, and that his manner was not only deferential, but slightly anxious and nervous and embarrassed, as if he were a needy tradesman eager to propitiate a difficult customer. Moreover, he was unctuously and little less than stickily profuse in compliments, pouring them forth with a liberality which reminded one of oil dripping from a castor-bean press. He repeated over and over such lubricating commonplaces as, "I thank you truly, Mr. Vane. You are really much too kind. You do me too high an honor. This from you, my dear sir, is more than I deserve. I am delighted to have the pleasure of your acquaintance. I hope to learn statesmanship from you, sir. I trust that you will find me a zealous scholar. We have all been, as it were, waiting for you. O, thank you kindly!" when a seat was urged upon him. "You are really too urbane and thoughtful. I thank you heartily."

At last, emerging with difficulty from a wilderness of bowings and scrapings, they all three got settled creakily on such unstable chairs as the dingy parlor afforded. Mr. Dorman now opened his dry, blackened, baked lips, and took the lead in the conversation.

"Just in Washington, Vane. I came on about my little job, and I thought I'd drop in to see how you found yourself; and as I was strolling along I met Friend Sharp."

Here he glanced at that worthy person, who was thereby driven to nod and smile in confirmation of the tale, although the fact was that Dorman had looked him up at his residence and besought him eagerly to call on Vane.

"And it's a lucky circumstance, I think," continued Darius, with one of his unpleasing smiles, — a grimace which seemed to express suffering rather than joy, as though he had sat down upon an unhealed burn. "You see, Friend Sharp is one of the oldest sailors in this ship of state, and knows all the ropes, and the way to the caboose, and everything."

"O, Mr. Dorman! you do me too much honor!" put in Mr. Sharp, with a meek, uneasy air. "I scarcely know a rope, and know nothing about the caboose. You are really too obliging. But you mean a compliment, and I thank you kindly."

"I must have my little joke," winked Darius. "Well, at any rate, Friend Sharp is a man who knows how to keep out of traps and to show others how to steer clear of them. Now you, Vane, have got a great measure on your mind and conscience. It's a great and good measure; there's no use in disputing it. The only question is, whether it is best to push it now, or wait awhile. Will hurrying it up do good or do harm? Mr. Simon Sharp is just the person to tell you."

"Well, gentlemen," said Vane, with an elevating sense of making a revelation, while the truth was that Sharp already knew all about his proposed bill — "well, gentlemen, I want to abolish the franking privilege."

The member from the old Whetstone State bowed, stretched out one of his smiles into an adulatory grin, and whispered in his greasiest voice, "Certainly, Mr. Vane, certainly!"

"You agree with me!" rejoiced Honest John. "Well, I'm glad of securing one leading voice in the House."

"In principle — in principle," Mr. Sharp continued to grin; "yes, in principle I entirely agree with you. You have suggested a measure which touches my conscience, and I need not say that I thank you kindly. You will find many sympathizers with your idea in Congress, sir.

118

All honest, fair-minded, intelligent, and patriotic members long to do away with that expensive nuisance which so corrupts our national morality and overloads our mail-bags. The trouble is that the fellows who want a re-election —" And here the good soul shook his venerable head sadly over the character of the fellows who wanted a re-election.

"But ain't there enough popular men and sound patriots to carry it, in spite of those chaps?" asked Vane, anxiously.

"You see, there are *so many* who want a re-election!" explained Mr. Sharp, gently. "In fact, almost everybody gets around to that state of mind after two years."

"Do you mean to say that all Congressmen think of is how to get another term?" exclaimed Honest John, rather indignant at the insinuation.

"No, no, by no means!" implored the Whetstone State representative. "Pray don't understand me as even suggesting such a calumny. They think of many other things," he added, remembering certain objects of general interest which he did not choose to mention; "but this particular measure, you see — the stoppage of electioneering documents, etc.—touches every man's chances in the end."

"I see it does," grumbled our upright and brave member. "But what has that got to do with a fellow's duty?"

This allusion to duty may not have seemed germane or important to Mr. Sharp; at all events he did not give himself the trouble to oil it with any commentaries.

"Horace Greeley worked at this abuse for years," he pursued. "Horace was an honest politician and a very potent editor. He did his best, and he failed."

"And you mean to say that a man who isn't a shaving to Horace Greeley won't succeed any better than he did," inferred John Vane, with a lowliness which shows that he had some sense.

"I don't mean to say that you are only a shaving to Mr. Greeley," responded Mr. Sharp, politely. "By no means, sir. On the contrary, you quite remind me of Mr. Greeley," he added, running his eyes over Vane's cherubic face and portly figure. "He was not so well-favored a man as you, sir; but still you remind me of him, — remind me very agreeably. Both self-made men, also; I say it with profound respect." He bowed here, and indeed he kept bowing all the while, like an earthenware mandarin. "And both honest, known to the world as such, eminent for it!" he emphasized, with a grin which could have bitten a quarter out of a mince-pie. "Ah, well, sir! so much the worse!" he resumed. "An honest man can't do away with the franking privilege. A rogue might, for he would offer something in place of it, and so, perhaps, carry his point by a sort of bargain. No, Mr. Vane; you must really excuse me for contradicting your honorable hopes, but a gentleman of your character can't repeal the franking privilege, — at least not for years to come. That is my sorrowful, but candid belief."

John Vane stared at Mr. Simon Sharp with wonder and dismay. The venerable man had begun all right on this matter, and then in the most rational and natural manner, had ended all wrong. Was this the way that people learned to reason by dint of sitting for several terms in Congress?

"If you could only become useful, — generally useful, you understand, — you might try your bill with some chance of success," resumed Mr. Sharp, after some moments of meditation. "A man who is known to be *useful*," — and he laid a very strong emphasis on the word, — "such a man can propose almost anything, and carry — well, carry something."

"Well, how can I get to be useful?" inquired the zealous neophyte from Slowburgh.

"I'll tell you," smiled the veteran, at the same time hitching his chair forward confidentially, as if being useful were a sort of patent-right or other precious secret, not to be communicated to the public.

"SPECIAL legislation is the great field for what I call Congressional *usefulness*," pursued Mr. Sharp, again bringing down a violent emphasis on the word, as if he were trying to drive it into his listener's head.

"Ah! is it?" stared John Vane. "That's news to me. I thought general legislation was the big thing, — reform, foreign relations, sectional questions, constitutional points, and so on; I thought those were the diggings to get a reputation out of."

"All exploded, my dear sir!" answered Mr. Sharp. "All gone out with Calhoun and Webster, or at the latest, with Lincoln and Stanton. All dead issues, as dead as the war. Special legislation — or, as some people prefer to call it, finance — is the sum and substance of Congressional business in our day. It is the great field, and it pays for the working. It pays every way. Your vote helps people, and they are grateful and help *you*. Your vote brings something to pass, and the public sees that it does, and respects you. Work into finance, Mr. Vane," exhorted Mr. Sharp, gently moving his hand in a spiral, as if to signify the insinuation of a corkscrew, "work slow - ly into — finance — so to call it. Take up some great national enterprise, and engineer it through. Get your name associated with a navigation scheme, or a railroad scheme, to advance commerce, you understand, or to move the crops." And as he alluded to these noble purposes, his voice became little less than reverential. "The millions yet unborn — you understand," here he seemed to be suggesting hints for a speech in advocacy of said scheme, — "millions yet unborn will have reason to remember you. Capital will become your friend. And capital — ah, Mr. Vane, there's a word! My very blood curdles when I think of the power and majesty of *capital*. This land, sir, this whole gigantic Republic, with its population of forty millions, its incomparably productive and energetic industry, and its vast network of continental communications, is the servant, and I had almost said the creature, of *capital*. Capital guides it by its wisdom and sustains it by its beneficence. Capital is to be, and already is, its ruler. Make capital your friend. Do something for it, and secure its gratitude. Link your fortunes and your name with some gigantic financial enterprise. Then, when you have won the reputation of advancing the industrial interests of the country, and gathered around you hosts of admirers and friends, you can return to your pet measure. Now, there is my advice — the advice of an old hand. Doesn't it strike you as worth considering? My maxim, as you see, is slow and sure. I also have my little reform at heart, but I keep it waiting until I can get strong enough to push it, and meantime I strengthen myself by helping other people. Never mind now what that reform is," he added, noting a gleam of inquiry in Vane's eye; "you will hear of it some day. Let us come to the immediate and the practical. While I make my humble little project bide its time, I am busy with a scheme which combines capital and industry, a scheme of national importance and magnitude. I don't mind mentioning it to you. It is the great Subfluvial Tunnel Road, meant to run through our country from north to south, under the Mississippi River, uniting Lake Superior with the Gulf of Mexico. It is a gigantic idea: you must admit it. Of course, the business minutiæ and prospects of it are beyond me," he conceded, with an air of innocence and simplicity which seemed to relieve him of all responsibility as to those points. "There I have to trust to the judgment of business men. But where my information fails, Mr. Dorman here can fill the gap. Dorman, suppose you let our friend into this if he wants to come in."

John Vane, being quite beyond his honest depth by this time, had nothing to say to the Great Subfluvial either in condemnation or praise, but merely stared in expectant silence.

"It is the job I gave you a hint about in Slowburgh," began Darius Dorman, turning upon his member a pair of sombre, lurid, smoky eyes, which were at once utterly unearthly and utterly worldly. "We have just got it well under way."

"What! stock taken?" exclaimed Vane, amazed that he had not heard of such a huge financial success.

Darius smiled, as a slave-trader might smile upon a stalwart, unsuspicious negro who should express a curiosity to see the interior of his schooner.

"The subscription is to be started by the government," he proceeded. "That is, the government will loan the capital necessary to build the tunnel, and then secure itself by a mortgage on the same. No particular risk, you see, to capitalists, especially as they will get the first issue of stock cheap, and won't be called on to pay in a heavy percentage. What they don't want to keep they can sell to the outside public, — the raft of small investors. Now, bankers and financiers won't neglect such a chance as that; they will pile in as fast and as plenty as need be. With a government loan to start on, the stock is sure to be floated and the thing finished; and after that is done, why, it will go on pretty much as railroads do, — gradually increase its business, and in the end pay well, like railroads."

Just here there was a malicious twinkle in his charcoal-pits of eyes, as though he were thinking of the numberless widows and orphans and other unprotected creatures whose little all had gone into railroads without ever bringing out a dividend. At the same time, he glanced suddenly at his grimy hands and rubbed them uneasily against each other, as if he would have been glad to get them clean for once in his existence, or as if the maculations on them itched and scalded quite intolerably.

"O, there's nothing unusual or extra smart about the enterprise!" he resumed, perhaps detecting in Honest John Vane's countenance a gleam of suspicion. "It's about the way railroads in general are got up, except the one notion of a government loan to start the thing. That is new and patented. Don't mention that for the Devil's sake!" he implored, with an outburst of his characteristically eccentric profanity. "Keep as dark as hell about the whole thing. All we want of you is to bear the job in mind, and when the House comes to the question of the loan, give us your voice and vote."

"It will be a grand thing for the country," put in Mr. Sharp, seeing that Vane pondered.

"O, magnificent!" exclaimed Dorman. "Give us another New York at New Orleans. Double the value of land in the Mississippi Valley."

"Unite the North and South," continued Sharp. "Close up the bloody chasm. Bind together the national unity in chains of cast-iron."

"Pour the wild rice of Green Bay upon the dinner-tables of our working-men," responded Dorman.

"Bring the Menomonie Indians within easy reach of Christian missionaries," was Sharp's next word in this litany.

"Providing the whole tribe hasn't already got to the happy hunting-grounds," suggested Dorman.

The Whetstone statesman glanced at the business man, and the business man glanced at the Whetstone states-man. Apparently (only John Vane did not perceive it) the two came very near laughing in each other's faces.

"Besides, it will pay well, at least to first investors," resumed Dorman.

"Yes, I should think it might pay *them* well," answered John Vane, with just a suspicion of satire in his tone.

"If you should ever care to invest, by the way," suggested the business man, as though that were a thing which he had just thought of, and which would of course not influence his representative's decision, "if you should ever fancy putting something of your own in, we can promise you a sure return for it. You shall have your pick, — stock at the opening figure, — corner lots cheap around the stations, — something paying and safe, you know, something salable if you don't want it."

"Well, I'll think of it," nodded Vane, who had already made up his honest mind to have nothing to do with the Great Subfluvial, judging it to be a scheme for swindling the government and the general public.

"Do so," begged Mr. Simon Sharp, his broad array of yellow teeth showing in a manner which vaguely reminded one of the phrase, "dead men's bones and all uncleanness." The member from the old Whetstone State seemed at the moment to be as full of teeth as ever a freshly opened tomb was of skeletons. It was an error in him to make exhibition of those ravening tushes and grinders; they neutralized abominably the expression of integrity and piety which gleamed from the Puritanic lacker of his venerable mug. "Do, Mr. Vane," he continued, "give the project your intelligent consideration, and see if it is not worthy of your highly reputable and valuable support. And now, sir, I am compelled, very much against my wishes, to bid you a good morning. Delighted to have made your acquaintance, and to welcome you as a brother Congressman. Don't go to the door with me, don't! You are altogether too urbane. I thank you kindly."

"HONEST, able old fellow, that Sharp," observed Dorman, as soon as the Whetstone patriot had fairly bowed and smirked himself out of the house. "Glad he happened to drop in on you while I was here."

"See here, Darius!" broke out Vane, still Honest John Vane, proud of his noble *sobriquet* and resolved to hold fast to it. "I'm not going to go for a bill merely because there's money in it, and some of that money offers to come my way. That ain't my style."

"I know it isn't," conceded Dorman, bowing humbly to this tempest of integrity and honorable self-esteem, probably for the sake of weathering it sooner.

"Then what do you offer me cheap stock for, and corner lots at a nominal figger, and all that sort of thing, to get me to vote your loan? Don't you know and don't I know that you are trying to bribe me?"

"You take your risk, don't you?" argued the man of affairs. "I don't offer you money, but merely a business risk."

"What risk is there when the government is to construct the road, and to give it such a credit that the stock can't help selling? You might as well talk about the risk of taking United States bonds at half the market value. You can't fool me that way, old boy. I'm a business man myself. I see as plainly as you do that the Great Subfluvial is to be built at the expense of the Treasury for the benefit of directors and officers and boss stockholders, who will take the shares at fifty, say, and sell them out at par, and then leave the whole thing on the hands of the small investors and Uncle Sam. That's what you fellows mean to do, and want me to help you do. I don't see it."

"John Vane, if you are really Honest John Vane, you'll allow that one good turn deserves another," insinuated Dorman.

"I know you think you put me here," replied Vane, who already began to feel the oats on which Congressmen feed, and to attribute to his own mettle his advancement from the position of "wheel-horse" to that of "leader." "You did say a word in season for me at the caucus: I own it. But proposing is one thing, and getting the nomination is another, and carrying the election is a third. Could you have shoved through any other man? Why didn't you try it? You saw what horse could win the race, and you bet on it. It was the name of Honest John Vane, — the man of the plain people, — the self-made man, — that's what took the caucus and the ballot-boxes. And now you want me to throw all those claims to respect and power overboard; want me to stop being honest and to tax the plain people uselessly; want me to go back on myself and my best friends; want me to follow in Bummer's dirty trail. Suppose I should do it? Why, I should end like Bummer; I should be laid on the shelf. O, I'm not ungrateful for what you did toward the nomination! I'll do anything in reason for you, old boy, — get you a collectorship or postmastership, anything that'll bear telling of. But I won't help plunder the Treasury of forty millions, and the stock-buying public of twice as much more, merely to give you a hundred thousand and myself five thousand. I tell you squarely, and you may as well understand it first as last, that I won't go into your lobbying."

"Why, this is the way everything works here," the lobbyist (for such he was) at last asserted in his desperation. "Bills of this sort slide through every year. Some are upset, but who upsets them? Fellows who haven't been retained, or who have rival bills to push. I tell you, John Vane, that more than half your brother patriots in the Capital do something in this line. The main work of Congress is done out of sight, like that of a mole, or by Beezlebub! any other underground creature. Making such laws as are needed, and voting such appropriations as the departments demand, wouldn't worry through a ten day's session. The real business of your legislators is running party politics, clearing scores with your fuglemen, protecting vested interests which can pay for it, voting relief bills for a percentage on the relief, and subsidizing great schemes for a share of the subsidy. A good Congressman of the present day is the silent partner of every job that he supports. That's what I meant by financial legislation when I urged you to go into it. Don't be an old-fashioned dog-in-the-manger, John Vane. Go with the crowd and humor the crowd; let others have their fodder, and bite in yourself. Look at the rafts of patriot statesmen who drive their carriages and keep open house. Do you suppose they do it off their salaries? Then why can't you do it off your salary, instead of huddling into these two little rooms and traveling by horsecar? Is it because they know how to make money go further than you do? No, *sir!* They take their little stock in a good bill, and then put it through. It's the common thing in Washington, and it's got to be the correct thing. And *you* can't change it. There's a boiler inside this boat which will make the wheels turn round, no matter who tries to hold 'em. As long as there is special legislation, there will be money to be made by it, and legislators will take their share. When a rich financier or monopolist comes to a poor M. C., and whispers to him, I want a chance to pocket a million, is the M. C. to say, Pocket it, and be sure not to give me any? Will he, as your human nature averages, will he say it? No, *sir!* he says, Let me have a percentage; and I assert that he's right. It's the natural working of humanity, under the circumstances. The only thing I wonder at is, that Congressmen are content with so little. Most of 'em ain't bold and hearty at all. They are pusillanimously half honest. Come, Vane, I want you to do well in the world of politics, and I want you to begin by supporting the Great Subfluvial."

"Dorman, I have the greatest mind in the world to expose you," was the almost heroic response of Honest John.

"I should contradict and disapprove every word of your exposure," laughed the unabashed lobbyist. "Do you suppose Congress wants subsidy legislation ripped open and exhibited to the public? Congress would believe you and would appoint a committee of investigation, and then would hush the matter up. Wait till you have learned your business, and then call me a liar, if you can."

And so the interview ended, with virtue still unshaken, but vice undiscouraged. Darius Dorman was too familiar with his evil trade and with the society in which it had hitherto prospered, to despair of finally leading his representative up to the manger of corruption. He narrated the substance of the above dialogue to the Honorable Simon Sharp with spasmodic twinges of cheerless gayety which resembled the "cracked and thin laughter heard far down in Hell."

"It is ludicrous, I must confess, Mr. Dorman," sighed the representative of the old Whetstone State, with a sad shake of his venerable long head; "but painfully so. I'm afraid that your friend won't come to much in Congress. He won't be a practical statesman. No head for finance."

"Don't give way to despondency about him, my benevolent creature," answered Darius, shaking all over with his dolorous mirth, his very raiment, indeed, quivering and undulating with it, so that it seemed as if there might be a twitching tail inside his trousers. "I have looked into the very bottom of John Vane's thimbleful of soul. I know every sort and fashion of man that he will make up into, under the scissoring of diverse circumstances. John has no character of his own. He has had neither the born twist nor the education to give him one. He is a chameleon. He takes the color of the people about him. If his constituents ever find him out, they won't call him Honest John Vane, but Weathercock John. He went straight in Slowburgh, because most folks in Slowburgh go straight. After he has been long enough in Congress he will be like the mass of Congressmen. The furnace of special legislation and the bellows of Washington opinion will melt him over. Don't be anxious about him; it is a mere matter of time. He is pious, I grant; but so are you, Friend Sharp; so are lots more who live by subsidy bills. It's of no use to be inside religion when you are also inside politics, as politics now go. Yes, it *is* of use; it varnishes the politics over nicely; it makes the special legislation look decent. John will be a great help to us, his reputation is so good. We must keep going for him, and we shall finally fetch him. When he finds that the majority take stock in bills, when he fairly realizes that he must choose between failing as a watchdog of the Treasury and succeeding as lapdog of the lobby, he will go for the spoils solid, or at least vote a split ticket. I'll bet on bringing him over; I'll bet my eternal happiness on it!" he laughed, as though the article in question were not much to risk.

"You are a very plain-spoken person, Mr. Dorman," observed the Honorable Sharp, pulling a decorously long face. "Just a little — well, let us say eccentric, in your expressions," he added with his obsequious smile. "However, to come to the substance of what you tell me, I must admit that it is encouraging. You really cheer me, Mr. Dorman. I thank you kindly."

Well, we have described the first Washingtonian temptation which stole to the side and whispered in the ear of Honest John Vane. Of course it was not the last; the goblins of the Mammonite crew dropped in upon him from week to week and almost from day to day; he could hardly put out his hands without feeling the pocket of a ring or corporation gaping to receive them. If he accepted an invitation to a supper, he found that it was given by some subsidy or relief bill. If a gentleman offered him a cigar, he discovered that it was scented with appropriations. If he helped a pretty woman into a street car, she asked him to vote for her statue or her father's claim.

The lobby proved to be every way more imposing and potent than he had imagined it. True, some of its representatives were men whom it was easy for him to snub, — men of unwholesome skins, greasy garments, brutish manners, filthy minds, and sickening conversation; men who so reeked and drizzled with henbane tobacco and cockatrice whiskey that a moderate drinker or smoker would recoil from them as from a cesspool; men whose stupid, shameless boastings of their briberies were enough to warn away from them all but the very elect of Satan. But there were other corruptionists whom he could not steel himself to treat rudely. There were former members of Congress whose names had been trumpeted to him by fame in his youthful days; decayed statesmen, who were now, indeed, nothing but unfragrant corpses, breeding all manner of moral vermin and miasma, but who still had the speech of patriotism on their lips and the power to argue speciously about the "needs of the country." There were dashing Brummels, who seemed to him much finer gentlemen than himself, asserting a high position in society, wearing fine raiment elegantly, brilliant in conversation, gracious in manner, and stately in port. There were soldiers of the late war, bearing titles which made his civilian history appear mean, and boasting of services which seemed to crown them with a halo of patriotism.

Hardest of all for a novice in public affairs to face, there were pundits in constitutional law and Congressional precedent, whose deluges of political lore overflowed him like a river, and stranded him promptly on lone islands of silence. Then there were highly salaried and quick-witted agents of great business houses, which he, as a business man, knew, respected, and perhaps feared. Now and then, too, there was a woman, audacious and clever and stylish and handsome, — an Aspasia who was willing to promise money, and able to redeem her promises in beauty. Indeed, it sometimes seemed to John Vane that the lobby was a cleverer and more formidable assemblage than either of those two chambers which nominally gave laws to the nation. More and more distinctly, as the session went on, he realized that his honesty would have a hard fight of it, and that if he succeeded in keeping it from being borne to the ground, he would grandly deserve to wear his cherished *sobriquet*.

IN short, Honest John Vane was so abundantly tempted and harassed by the lobbyists and their Congressional allies, as to remind us of that hardly bested saint whom we have all seen in ecclesiastical pictureland, surrounded by greater and lesser goblins and grotesque manifestations of Satan.

Virtue was the harder for him to follow after, because he perceived that the vicious were not only enviably prosperous, but walked in their evil ways undiscovered. The skinny leanness of his own honest *porte monnaie* was all the more obvious to him when he contrasted it with the portly pocket-books of the slaves of the ring. While he foresaw that it would be difficult for him to bring the year around on his salary, there was Potiphar of New Sodom taking in one hundred thousand dollars for "putting through" a single bill. While his brilliant Olympia was sitting solitary and sorrowful in her two dingy rooms, plain Mrs. Job Poor, the wife of a member who supported the iron interest, kept open house in a freestone block, and rolled in her carriage. It seemed to him at times that, if there was a city on earth where integrity got all the kicks, and knavery all the half-pence, that city was the capital of this model Republic.

Nevertheless, he held fast by his righteousness and remained worthy of his reputation. Give a dog a bad name and he will deserve it, says one of the wisest of proverbs. It is equally true that if you give a dog a good name, he will strive to deserve that. In these days, when temptation sought to bow Vane into the dirt, it was a greatly supporting circumstance to him that he had received the title of Honest. Now and then he was cheered and strengthened by seeing himself eulogized in the newspapers under this Catonian epithet. Occasionally, too, the organ of a ring would boast (falsely) that honest John Vane had decided to vote for its particular swindle, — a fact which showed that the name had become a synonyme for respectability and was reckoned able to carry weight. He was a better man for this honorable "handle"; it had the elevating influence of a commission as "an officer and a gentleman"; it inspired him to exemplify the motto, *Noblesse oblige*. In spite of recurring enticements, he struggled on through the session, without letting his hands be soiled by the first dirty dollar.

In the meantime, his dear Olympia had been a greater trial and stumbling block to him than the lobby. Not that she consciously meant to trip up his integrity; on the contrary, she hardly gave a serious thought to it. Her desire was that her husband should take the political leadership which belonged to him, and, what was of course much more important, should give her the fashionable eminence which belonged to her. She had early discovered, to her amazement and disappointment and vexation, that a Congressman was not necessarily a social magnate in Washington. If he was rich or potent, he was reverenced; if he was poor and uninfluential, he was neglected: his mere office had little to do with the matter. There were members whom the legislative world and the stylish world did not make obeisance to; and of these members, her John, whom she had partly selected because of his supposed greatness, was one. She soon found that the wives of Cabinet secretaries and of senators and of the chiefs of the great committees regarded her as their inferior. Many of them did not ask her to their receptions, and only returned her calls by sending cards. Spurred by her eager desire to commune with the ultra genteel, she committed the imprudence of attending one senatorial party without an invitation, and was treated with such undisguised *hauteur* by the hostess that she went bedridden with mortification for three days.

Even her beauty, which had secured her so many university beaux in Slowburgh, seemed to have no charm here. Few noted gentlemen called on her, and not many of these called twice. Whenever by good luck she got to a reception, there was no swarming of fascinated male creatures about her, and she was free to pass the entire evening on the arm of her husband. She had anticipated romantic attentions from foreign secretaries, and perhaps ambassadors; but at the end of the session she did not know a single member of any one of the diplomatic corps; the only alien individuals who came with music to her windows were monkeys and their masters. For a time this neglect was a puzzle to her, and personally a most humiliating one. Her beauty and graces were so obviously ineffective that she began to doubt whether she possessed beauty or grace, and to feel in consequence that she was of no worth, and even contemptible.

Eventually, however, she obtained light on this subject; she perceived that her husband was right in affirming that everybody in Washington "had an axe to grind";

the natural result being, that gentlemen would not spend their time in paying court to ladies whose male relatives had no favors to confer. At first it was a dismaying discovery, and she very nearly wept with vexation over it, and tried to despise the world for its sordid selfishness. But before long, moved by her habitual reverence for society, she drifted into a disposition to take it as she found it, and would fain have won its homage by a show of that wealth and power which it demanded. The first step to this end, of course, was to get out of her commonplace lodgings and ascend to a grander style of living.

"O, I do hate these dirty, poverty-stricken barracks!" she moaned, more bitterly than ever. "I see plainly that we shall never be anybody in Washington as long as we pen ourselves up in two little vile rooms. You ought to take a house, John, and give receptions and dinners, for the sake of your own career. You would get a great deal more influence that way than by fussing over papers in committees and making speeches."

Then followed the old, stale discussion over the expense of such a route to glory, the husband ending with his usual meek but firm declaration that he dared not risk it. Thereupon Olympia cried harassingly for an hour or more, and sulked in silence for a day or two. It seemed as if some alien and naughty soul had migrated into her since the engaged days when she rayed forth graciousness and amiability. The broad fact is that, so far as the masculine outsider can discover, most girls have no character until marriage. Then for the first time they enter openly upon the struggle for life, and then the strong traits which have hitherto remained invisible come out boldly, like certain chemical inks when exposed to the fire.

The result of this severest of Olympia's many sulkings was a compromise. John Vane held on in his frugal or semi-frugal lodgings, but he allowed his wife to give frequent dinners, and also evenings with ice-cream. But such a lame, halt, and beggarly lot as appeared at these cheap, cold-water festivities! It seemed as if the host must have gone out deliberately into the highways and hedges of political life and forced them to come in. There were Congressmen who were just like John himself, — mere tyros and nobodies in the great world of statesmanship, members of the little committees or of no committee at all. There were members from carpetbagdom who had not yet secured their seats, and delegates from the territories who looked as though they might represent the Digger Indians. Occasionally there was a sharp wire-puller or a sturdy log-roller from Slowburgh, and more rarely a respectable citizen of that place, who had come on to stare around Washington. One evening Olympia was nearly driven into hysterics of mortification by discovering that her husband had brought in a Mormon. She treated the venerable representative from Utah as she had herself been treated at Senator Knickerbocker's, and subsquently informed Honest John several dozen times that he had ruined their position in society.

"I thought the old fellow would be a curiosity and amuse you," pleaded the husband. "You are always saying you want amusement."

"Not that kind," tossed Olympia, utterly out of patience with his stupidity, and thinking that by this time he ought to have comprehended her better. "Low people may amuse you, and I know they do. It is really one of the great faults of your character, John. But to me they are simply strange and odious bores. Can't you understand, once for all, that I want such amusements as other ladies want, — good society and genteel surroundings and — and nice things?"

"O, yes; and you want to dine with the British Ambassador, and ride in a coach with liveries," grumbled John, restive under this pestering, because he was yet sore with preceding ones.

"Well, what woman in Washington doesn't?" retorted Olympia, justifying herself in her own eyes with lamentable facility.

"I suppose you don't think there's anything fine in having an honest man who does his duty and nothing but his duty," groaned Vane, referring with pardonable pride to himself, but fretting under the knowledge that his wife did not share that pride.

"O, there are so many honest people," sniffed Olympia, eager to "take him down." — "They are as common as chips."

"Not in Washington," returned this unappreciated Aristides, with a bitterness which was only in part patriotic.

Such little tiffs as this, I regret to avow, soon became frequent. Olympia, having discovered that potentiality in politics was necessary as a basis for social eminence, began to interest herself disagreeably in her husband's Congressional doings, and to rub peppery remarks into him concerning his obligation to be eloquent, able, managing, and, in short, successful. She informed herself as to what committees were the important ones, and demanded of him why he was not on any of them.

"Because I am a young member, I suppose," answered John, a little sulkily; for the fact in itself was an irritating one, let alone being "talked to" about it.

"But here you are on the Committee for Revolutionary

Pensions," persisted the ambitious lady. "It is almost an insult. There are only three or four Revolutionary pensioners left. Of course there is nothing to do."

"Well, we do nothing," granted John, ungraciously. "Somebody must do it."

"You ought to try to get on the Committee of Ways and Means, Mrs. Bullion says," continued Olympia. "That is the great committee, she says. Why don't you?"

"Why don't I try to be President?" exclaimed Vane. "I *am* trying, I am doing what work comes in my way as thoroughly and honestly as I can. If I stay here long enough, I suppose I shall get higher," continued the poor catechised man, who really had in him some industry, perseverance, and common sense, — materials of character which might in time be worked up into a fair law-giver.

"Why don't you push your bill about that — that privilege?" was the next question of this stateswoman. "That would make a sensation."

"They smothered it in committee," confessed the husband. "What could I do after that?"

"There! now you see!" exclaimed Olympia. "You see the need of being on the leading committees. If you had been a member of *that* committee, you could have stopped their smothering it."

"No, I couldn't," contradicted John, naturally indignant at being blamed for everything, both what he did and what others did. "If I had been on it, I should have been a minority of one, and the bill would have been smashed all the same. The fact is, that Congressmen in general are determined to hold on to the franking privilege."

"Didn't I tell you?" cried Olympia, remembering that

she had once counselled him not to urge unpopular measures, — "didn't I tell you so before we were engaged, and ever so many times since? I told you to give up that old thing and plan something that could pass. O, I wish *I* was a man!"

Remembering that if she had been one, he should not have fallen in love with her, Vane was tempted to reply, "I second the motion." But he restrained himself, for he had a magnanimous streak in him, and he was really very fond of his wife.

12

IN these days, Olympia was both sore and prickly with a consciousness of her husband's incapacity; she was as uncomfortable and as discomforting as a porcupine might be whose quills should be sharp at both ends.

She was always comparing him disparagingly with somebody, — with that well-descended gentleman of the old school, Senator Knickerbocker; or that opulent gentleman of a new school, Senator Ironman; with the Speaker and the chairman of the Finance Committee, and that elegant Potiphar who had taken the hundred thousand dollar fee; with the noted orators who had the ear of the House, such as General Boum and General Splurge.

She still liked John — in lonely moments; when they were by themselves of an evening, she often clung to him with a sense that it was sweet to be loved and protected; but all day she wished that he were more respected than he was, and greater than he could be. At times she had an idea, or perhaps I should say a feeling, that he had palmed himself off on her by false pretences. Had he not married her in the guise of a political giant, and was he not an indisputable political dwarf? Other men made great speeches which stormed the admiration of Washington, or "engineered something through Congress" which had the effect of putting their wives into freestone mansions. Not so with her husband; he was a nobody, politically, socially, and financially; and it was all his fault, too, for *she* wanted it different.

But, at last, and as if by a mere freak of fortune, a beam of prosperity lighted her path. Senator Ironman, who was worth two millions at least, encountered her by chance at a reception, paid her some flattering attentions, called upon her a few days later, and cajoled his wife into calling. Glad and proud indeed was Olympia over the acquisition of this patrician intimacy, the pass to all the selectest dress circles and most exclusive private boxes of that complex theatre, the social life of Washington. Finally her beauty had availed her somewhat; it had brought her in an hour more that was of value in her eyes than she had derived in many months from her husband's public services and reputable name; and, as beauty triumphant will do, it bloomed out with increased splendor.

John Vane thought that he had never seen his wife so handsome as she was on the evening in which he took her to Ironman's great party, the grandest crush of the season. It was even very delightful to the honest, unsuspecting soul to note how the rich and arrogant senator evidently admired her, and how much he walked and waltzed with her. And, if Mr. Vane liked it well, you may be sure that Mrs. Vane liked it better. She was throbbingly happy, whether on the great man's arm in the promenade, or on his shoulder in the dance. The deep flush of her brunette cheeks and the liquid sparkle of her dark eyes revealed a stronger agitation than had possessed her for many a day. People stared at her a good deal; they called her "a stunner," and thought her a little venturesome; various gentlemen, who knew Ironman well, exchanged queer glances; certain ladies, who were equally informed, gazed sidelong at Mrs. Ironman. None of these disquieting circumstances, however, were visible to our two innocents from Puritanic Slowburgh. They passed an entirely delightful evening, and then walked economically but contentedly home, telling each other how nice it had all been.

Thenceforward Mrs. Vane led a cheerier life of it. She was invited everywhere, and Mr. Ironman was always delightfully attentive, and consequently other people paid court. She no longer found the Washington receptions unsocial, heartless, and stupid, — mere elbowings of selfish people who either did not know each other, or only wanted to use each other, — the dreariest social gatherings perhaps that ever gas-light shone upon. The favor of the rich senator and of his adherents and parasites irradiated these doleful caucuses to her eyes with interest and gayety. Moreover, Mr. Ironman did not restrict his courtesies to occasions of festivity. His carriage (not his wife's, but his own special turnout) was frequently seen at Vane's humble door. He took Olympia in it all over the surrounding landscapes, to the reservoir hill back of Georgetown, to the soldiers' cemetery at Arlington, and to other similarly inspiring eminences whence one can see a great ways, though not into the future. Furthermore he gallanted her to the Capitol, to the Smithsonian, to the theatre, and to concerts. Likewise he sent her bouquets, and after a time finer presents. In fact, his assiduity gradually verged into such an appearance of courtship that there would have been talk about it, if Washington society had not been charitable even beyond Christianity in its judgments, and also absorbingly intent upon affairs which were more profitable than gossip.

It was, however, a perilous business for Olympia, this daily communion with Ironman. The senator was one of those infrequent and yet discoverable statesmen who value distinction among men mainly because it helps them to captivate women. Although he was, to speak with considerate vagueness, not under forty, he had that restless passion for "conquests" which we scarcely pardon in the novice of twenty, eager to secure acknowledgments of the puissance of his individuality, or, in other words, to show that he is "irresistible." There was not a session during which his proud, calm, mature Juno of a wife did not have occasion to wonder what sort of common mortal her Jove would run after next. This patient or indifferent lady, by the way, had taken very kindly to Olympia, considering her a young person whom it would be respectable for Ironman to drive about with, and who would keep him from making himself ridiculous by sending bouquets to treasury girls.

But absurd as the senator was in the eyes of his spouse, he could not seem absurd to Mrs. Vane, at least not immediately. His very rage for gallantry made him attractive to a woman who knew by experience the sweetness of flirtation, and who, for months past, had been confined to very short browsings of it. As for his shining state on the alps of society, and the entirely solvent, redeemable, coinable wreaths and vapors of opulence which hung about him, not only were they circumstances such as she had always looked up to with admiration, but they seemed more dazzling than ever, viewed through the atmosphere of Washington. It is true that this wealth was mainly the result of special enactments, not beneficial to the masses; that the rich statesman had enormously increased his riches by operations which he had himself helped to legalize; and that he had sometimes voted for a brother patriot's pet measure in consideration of a similar service rendered to his own. But Olympia did not concede much respect to political disinterestedness; she had had a surfeit of that poorly paying virtue in her own cheap and dingy home. Moreover, Ironman had always been so prosperous that he could afford to despise the direct lucre of the lobby, and thus had deserved, in the opinion of a closely sheared, patient public, the repute of being a singularly upright lawgiver.

Nor was this the end of his enchantments; he possessed talismans of a more personal nature. He was not so plain a man but that, by dint of careful grooming and fine caparisons, he could pass for handsome. True, he was too lean, too hollow in the chest, too narrow in the shoulders, and too knobby in the arms and legs, to inspire the most realistic sculptor with a desire to perpetuate his model in marble, except for the bare emoluments of the job. But like many tall and long-limbed men, he was graceful when under way, and had a specially good gait in dancing. As for the shiny circle on the top of his blonde head, it, at first sight, appeared a decided disadvantage. To conceal it he bowed rarely and at a very obtuse angle, which caused unobservant and unreflecting people to pronounce him haughty, if not discourteous. But, on the other hand, it led him to carry himself with erectness, and thus gave him a port which was generally admitted to be *distingué*. His long, aquiline, pinkish face had an expression akin to the immortal perplexity of Lord Dundreary, but for that very reason, perhaps, was considered patrician by numerous Washington ladies. On the whole, he was a cavalier whose proffered arm might well thrill an ambitious woman's heart with pride.

Such was the partially respectable statesman and almost entirely ludicrous man who lifted the Vanes into the highest circles of the society of our capital. As we have said, his favor was a perilous boon to Olympia, considering her breeding and aspirations. Even as a girl, even while living thriftily in staid Slowburgh, she had been eager after pomps and prodigalities. In Washington, she had become still more demoralized, if we may apply that ugly epithet to a longing for finery and admiration, — a longing so common among our "guardian angels." The splendors of women whose husbands had got fortunes by engineering schemes through Congress had completely dazzled her imagination and made her mad with envy.

It would seem that special legislation and its attendant snares of bribery were set for the downfall, not only of our Federal heads in Congress, but also of their Eves.

13

BY good fortune the intimacy between Senator Ironman and Olympia had budded so late in the session that it did not have time to ripen into such bloom as would irresistibly attract the eye of scandal.

John Vane went home quite content with his wife, and she rather more than content with herself. A diversified existence — Delectable Mountains mingled with Vales of Tears — awaited their feet in Slowburgh. It was delightful to our member to have his praises sung night and morning by the enamoured troubadours of the party journals, and to receive salaams, which were obviously tokens of respect for his proved uprightness, from men of acknowledged position and character, — men who had not previously deigned to know him, or had blandly kept him at a distance. On the other hand, it was disagreeable to listen to the grumblings of unrewarded wirepullers of low degree, and to feel obliged to pacify them by dint of promises, apologies, and wheedlings, which now for the first time seemed to him demeaning.

As for Olympia, she could at last enjoy a consciousness of peculiar distinction; for, whereas in Washington she had been only one of many Congresswomen, she was the sole and solitary one extant in Slowburgh, — a fact which gave her preeminence among her acquaintance. Unfortunately, it could not exalt her to the social zenith of Saltonstall Avenue, where political notoriety had long been considered a disqualification rather than an introduction, owing to its frequent connection with such low "jobbers" as Mr. James Bummer. Furthermore there was a scant supply in the family locker of money. During Vane's absence the refrigerator business had not done well; a costly patent in the same had proved unremunerative; the dividends were pitifully meagre. All the summer was spent in economizing at the maternal boarding-house or at a cheap resort by the seaside. It was impossible to meet the Ironmans at Saratoga, as Olympia had confidently agreed to do. You can imagine her general discontent and how frequently her husband suffered therefrom, and what a poorish season they had of it. But the summer and fall wore away at last, and they returned to Washington with a fair sense of satisfaction, though indifferently furnished in pocket.

"We must live mighty close this winter," said Vane to his wife, hoping she would take it well.

"Yes, we must keep house," replied Olympia, with cheerful firmness. "This lodging and boarding is awfully expensive, and you get nothing for your money, — a horrid table and vile furniture. It is just being swindled."

"I know it is being swindled," groaned John, gazing over the edge of the frying-pan into the fire. "But it is cheaper than housekeeping; everybody says so. We can't afford a house any more than we can afford a pyramid."

"Yes, we can," insisted Olympia. And thereupon she skipped lightly through a calculation of the cost of housekeeping: the rent would be so much, the food not much more, the service about half as much; the result a clear saving of many dollars a month.

It looked reasonable, when held up in that offhand way; it seemed as if economy might evolve such a consummation.

"But how about furniture, carpets, and so on?" reflected Vane.

"Why, take a furnished house, you muddled creature."

"Ah! but that doubles the rent, or comes closer to trebling it."

But still Olympia stuck to her project of saving; and at last (oh, the perseverance of wives!) she conquered. A house was taken, at first only for a month, for the rent scared Vane, and he would not sign a longer lease.

"It seems to me that you are just trying to clean me out," was his rather coarse response when Mrs. Vane pleaded for tenure by the session. "If we were only married for the season, I could understand it. Can't you remember that when my pocket is drained" (dreaned, he pronounces it) "yours is empty too?"

"And it seems to me that you are just trying to make me miserable," was Olympia's illogical but telling retort. "I don't want to be lectured, sir, as if I were in short dresses."

Nor was she singularly unreasonable. At that very time and perhaps in that very moment many other wives of Congressmen were inciting their husbands to spend more than their salaries. She had got into a lofty position, and she wanted to live conformably to it. That she should thus live seemed so rational to her, that she could not see how her husband could sanely object to it. As for the lack of sufficient income for the purpose, that surely was his lookout, and not hers. I ask triumphantly how many feminine intellects can discover a flaw in this logic?

Still, John showed no relenting; he had got his back up, as the tom-cats put it to each other; he even looked as though he did not care if she *were* miserable. So Olympia resorted to argument once more, as feeble humanity does when it finds grumbling useless. She recited the cases of half a dozen other members who had nothing but their salaries, yet took houses by the session; the inference being that her member could do likewise, and would if he were not a curmudgeon.

"Yes, and every one of them is head over heels in debt, or drawing bribes from every ring in the lobby," alleged Vane. "Do you suppose that being ruined in a crowd makes it any finer? Do you suppose that the drove of porkers who rushed down steep places into the sea found drowning any more comfortable because there were ten thousand of them?"

"Porkers! I should like to know whom you apply that name to," retorted Olympia, reddening with anger. "I am your wife, sir, and a born lady."

"I was speaking of Congress," answered Vane, with a smile, for he had grown tough under pecking. "Well, I see that there is no use in arguing this matter. I have signed the lease for one month, and I shall *not* change it."

So, on this occasion Olympia *had* to give in, although it almost cost her her life, to use a common exaggeration. But if a wife wants to punish her husband for his tyrannies, there are always ways enough to do it, thank gracious. Mrs. Vane signalized her first week of housekeeping by giving a costly dinner, inviting Senator Ironman thereto, and flirting with him so openly that henceforward John carried a fresh prickle in his hymeneal crown of roses. Other extravagances followed, not all of them indeed meant as castigations, for Olympia had a curious felicity at spending money, and did it literally without thinking. Instead of "saving on the table," as she had promised to do and really meant to do, she so managed matters as to make the family nourishment a synonyme in Vane's mind for being eaten out of house and home. Her cook did the marketing; for how could a born lady do it? And this cook was a Washington colored sister, — a fact which speaks volumes to naturalists acquainted with that primitive development of "help," — a fact which suggests waste, mousing relations, a hungry host of visitors in the kitchen, and perhaps pilfering. Vane asserted that, instead of feeding four people, as he had expected to do, he fed nearer fourteen. Mrs. Vane replied, sometimes tearfully and sometimes pettishly, that no mortal could rule "those creatures," and that no lady ought to be expected to do it.

Two months, however, had passed away before this state of things became obvious; the house being taken for a second month because "it seemed absurd to break up in such a hurry." Then, all of a sudden, our member found himself unable to pay his honest debts, or at least a portion of them. It was a terrible thing to him; never before had he been driven to send away a tradesman uncontent; and it took all his Congressmanhood to keep him from weeping over the novel humiliation. His distress was heightened by a daybreak dialogue which he chanced to overhear between his milkman and his butcher's driver.

"Say! what kind o' folks is these Vanes, anyway?" demanded the milkman, who was a Down-Easter settled in the District.

"Dunno," responded the driver, who was a colored man, and so cared for nobody and nothing.

"Waal, they've been gettin' milk from me for abeout nine weeks, an' don't seem to allude to no keind o' peay," continued the milkman, with a piteous, inquiring accent.

"Specs likely," admitted the negro, who would have thought strange of anybody offering to pay for anything.

The unmeant satire of these remarks stung Vane like a blister. All day he was saying to himself and of himself: "Don't seem to allude to no keind o' peay. Specs likely." He could not stand it; he must confide his troubles and ask advice; he must get strength, wisdom, and cheer out of somebody. The person whom he was finally moved to open his bosom to was not a brother legislator, but a person who was much scoffed at in Congress as a poetical enthusiast and a political idealist, because he was engaged in a noble plan for renovating a wofully decayed branch of the government. Mr. Frank Cavendish had met Vane in committee-rooms, and the two had been somewhat attracted to each other by their common unpopularity, both being reckoned stumbling-blocks to legislation as it is. To Cavendish our member now repaired, saying to himself in a pathetically meek spirit, that, if the man knew how to reform an entire system of official business, he might, perhaps, be able to reform a foolish Congressman.

"I don't want a loan," he explained, after he had stated his case. "That wouldn't get me out of debt; it would only change the debtor. Besides, it wouldn't stop the sinking process. What I want is to learn how to live on my salary, and still keep a decent position before the world. It wouldn't be a matter of much account if it was my case alone. But there are loads of us members in the same fix, getting deeper and deeper in debt every year, and seeing only one way out of it, — special legislation, you know."

This last phrase he added with a ready, commonplace wink which was habitual with him, and suggestive of character. It revealed that, while he disapproved of the briberies and corruptions of the lobby, he did not recoil from them with the disgust of a morally refined soul, and saw in them as much that was humorous as hideous.

"And that is sheer ruin," interjected Cavendish, with the haste of one who puts out his hand to save a man from falling.

"Yes, I suppose it *is*," responded Vane; remembering that if he should take bribes and be exposed in it, he would lose his prized and useful title of "honest."

"It is moral ruin to Congressmen and financial ruin to the country," continued Cavendish, wishing to impress his lesson clearly on this evidently doughy nature.

"You're right," admitted John, his conscience vitalized and his intellect cleared by the remark. "If things go on ten years as they are going now, the lobby will be the real legislative power of the land. Well, to come back to my own case, here I am living beyond my salary, and not very blamable for it either. I am *not* extravagant in my fancies," he affirmed positively, and, as we know, with truth; "and my wife don't want more than other women generally do," he added, giving Olympia what credit he might, and perhaps more than was her due. "But living here is really dear, — you can't make it otherwise. I've tried it, and you can't! I don't see but one salvation for us. Do you think it would do to make a move to raise our salaries?"

"Why not first make a move to lessen expenses?" suggested Cavendish.

"How?" asked Vane, thinking solely of giving up house-keeping and going into very cheap lodgings, and thinking at the same time of the strenuous fight which Olympia would wage against such a plan.

"Congress is largely to blame for the present enormous cost of living," continued Cavendish. "It devised and it still keeps in force the very laws which diminish by one half the purchasing power of the dollar. Congressmen vote to give themselves five thousand dollars a year, and then vote to make that sum equivalent to only twenty-five hundred. Of course *you* understand this matter," he added, politely imputing to Vane more political economy than was in him. "But allow me to explain myself, if only to relieve my own feelings. Here you legislative gentlemen refuse to hasten the resumption of specie payments. The consequence is, that you draw your salary in dollars which are worth only about ninety cents apiece. Next, and what is much more important, you keep up a system of taxation which benefits certain producers enormously, at an enormous expense to the collective body of consumers, the great majority of your constituents. Again, and this too is very important, you lay these taxes less on the luxuries of the rich than on the necessaries of the poor. You have made tea and coffee free, they being really luxuries and not needful to existence, although our extravagant working classes use them abundantly. Meanwhile you tax heavily all materials of labor and all articles of common comfort. There is hardly a substance or a tool which the American uses in his work but pays a heavy duty. His coal and lumber, his food and the salt which cures it, his clothing and so on, all are taxed. The result is that labor must get high wages or starve. The result to you is, that your apparently liberal salaries are insufficient to support a moderate style of living."

"O — I see — you are a free-trader," drawled John Vane, his countenance falling.

158

"No, I am an advocate of a revenue tariff; of a system of taxation which bears mainly on people in easy circumstances; of a system like that of England and Belgium. The entire public income of those two countries is paid by luxuries."

"O, I dare say you are right," sighed our member; "I haven't looked into it much, — I ain't on those committees, you know, — but I dare say you are right. However, it can't be helped." And he shook his law-giving head sadly. "If we should so much as whisper revenue tariff, all the monopolists, all the vested interests, would be after us. You don't know, perhaps, how sharp-eyed and prompt and powerful those fellows are. They are always on hand with their cash, and if you don't want that you do want re-election. They are as greedy, and I don't know but they are as strong, as the relief bill and subsidy chaps. It's a mean thing to own up to, but Congress daren't fight 'em. This country, Mr. Cavendish, this great Republic which brags so of its freedom, is tyrannized over by a few thousand capitalists and jobbers. No sir, it's no sort of use; we can't have a revenue tariff."

"Then there is nothing for an honest legislator to do but to live on the tough steaks and cold hominy of cheap boarding-houses," observed Cavendish.

"That's the only ticket," mumbled Vane; and the two patriots parted in low spirits.

14

AS Honest John walked homeward, eschewing the minute expense of the street-cars, he swore that he would live like a pauper, and so keep his integrity.

But he reckoned without his host, — meaning thereby the partner of his bosom, who was certainly a host in herself, particularly when it came to crying.

"Go back to boarding!" tearfully exclaimed Olympia, who just then had a reception in view. "Then why did you commence housekeeping? The idea of giving me a house only to take it away again! You don't love me as other men love their wives. You delight in plaguing me." And so on, and over again, with much sobbing.

In a day or two she actually impressed Vane with a feeling that, in wishing to "take her house from her," he was guilty of a purpose akin to robbery, and, of course, entirely unworthy of a just husband. He had to concede that, from one point of view, Olympia did not demand overmuch; even to his business-like and arithmetical imagination, five thousand dollars seemed a large income; even he could not yet believe it insufficient to cover housekeeping. Partly because he was deluded by this ante-tax idea, and partly because he was a compassionate man and loving husband, he deferred the humble and lenten pilgrimage through boarding-house deserts back to solvency, and, of course, went more and more laden with the bondage of debt.

At last, sad to relate, he began to admit to himself, like so many other hardly bested men, that "something or other must be done," meaning something which would bring money, no matter how. One evening as he sat alone in his parlor, now staring in dull discontent at the shaky furniture for which he paid such a high rent, now recalling the fact that Olympia was away at a reception with that opulently dazzling Ironman, he once more thought over his wilderness of troubles and tried to devise a way out of them. He was harassed, degraded, and enfeebled by the daily urgency of debt. His matrimonial happiness had been half wrecked by the mere lack of filthy lucre. If he wanted to recover his wife's respect and affection, he must positively provide her with gracious surroundings, and stop bullying her about expenditures. How could he get money, with honesty, or, alas! without it?

While he was puzzling amid the brambles of this wretched question, he was surprised by a visit from his former friend and wire-puller, Darius Dorman. Vane and Dorman had not seen much of each other since the former had denounced the Great Subfluvial Tunnel as little better than a trick for defrauding the government and the public of small investors. The lobbyist had judged that it would not be wise to "keep at" Honest John, and had expended his time, breath, and funds on members of a less Catonian type.

Meanwhile the bill had prospered as bills do which "have money in them." Although Vane had voted against it, the tunnel had obtained a charter from Congress and likewise a loan of forty millions from the United States

Treasury, the same being only a dollar a head from every inhabitant of this free country, including women, children, negroes, and Indians not taxed. Two or three times as many more millions had come in from financiers who saw forty per cent profit in an early purchase, and from a simple public which believed that it could safely follow the lead of the wise men of the capital. Furthermore, the directors and managers of the Great Subfluvial had contrived what might be called a Sub-Tunnel for their own peculiar emolument, which fulfilled its purpose admirably. This was a most wonderful invention, and deserves our intense study. It was a corporation inside of the original corporation. Its ostensible object was the construction of the Subfluvial, but its real object was the division of the capital into profits. For instance, it built a mile of tunnel at a cost of, say ten thousand dollars, and then delivered the same to the outside company for say fifty thousand dollars, and then shared the difference of forty thousand dollars among its own stockholders. Of course this was a better bargain for the inside company than for the outside one; but all chance of quarrelling between the two was evaded by a very effective device; they had the same men for directors, or the same men's partners.

O, it was a beautiful business idea, — this Floating Credit, or Syndicate, or whatever its inventors christened it. It reminds one of that ingenious machine called the Hen Persuader, which was so constructed that when placed under a hen's nest, it would withdraw every egg the moment it was laid, whereupon biddy would infer that her sensations had deceived her with regard to the fact of laying, and would immediately deposit another egg, and so continue to do until she died of exhaustion. In some respects, also, this internal corporation resembled that hungry creature known as a tape-worm, which devours a man's dinner as fast as he swallows it, and leaves him hungrier than ever.

Of course the gentlemen who held shares in the Hen Persuader did a profitable business, and filled their private wallets with golden eggs in abundance. But still they were not quite content; the old fowl above them, that is to say, Uncle Sam's eagle, occasionally cackled angrily; and it was extremely desirable to put a stop to his alarming demand for chickens. Darius Dorman had an anxious look on his crisped and smutted physiognomy as he seated himself opposite his representative.

"Vane, we must have another lift, or let the whole thing drop," he said abruptly.

"What! haven't you bled the treasury enough?" grumbled Honest John, angrily contrasting his own shrunken *porte monnaie* with the plethoric pocket-books and overrunning safes of the great corporation.

"We want time," answered Dorman, really meaning thereby that he wanted an eternity of it. "Here is this Secretary of the Treasury making a raid on us. He asks for interest on his loan. How in the name of all the witches of Salem does he suppose the Subfluvial can pay three millions of interest per year, in addition to meeting its running expenses? We understood that the interest was to wait until the termination of the loan, thirty years from now."

"Pay it out of the principal," suggested Vane sulkily. "Do as other roads do."

"But we want the principal for dividends. We can't keep on selling stock, unless we show a dividend now and then."

"Ain't there any profits?" asked Vane, with a keen look.

"Haven't your managers and inside passengers laid away enough to spare a little for profits?"

Dorman had such a spasm that he fairly writhed in his chair. It seemed as if every swindling dollar that he had got out of the Hen Persuader were that moment burning into his already cicatrized cuticle.

"O, they will fall in later," he smiled, recovering his self possession. "They will come when the tunnel is clean through, and has had time to make travel. But until that time arrives we must have favor shown us. Give us a lift, John, and we'll give you one."

Honest John Vane hesitated, querying whether he should take one solitary step to meet temptation, and see at least what it was like.

"Well," he at last said, in the surly tone of a man who feels that he is on the verge of making a diabolically bad bargain, — "well, what do you want now?"

THE very faint promise of aid which seemed to exhale from Vane's question cheered up Dorman a little.

There was a strange brightening in his dusky eyes, followed by a momentary obscuration and haziness, as though a few sparks had risen to their surface from some heated abyss, and had gone out there in a trifle of smoke. He started up and paced the room briskly for some seconds, meanwhile tightly clasping his dried-up, blackened claws across his coat-skirts, perhaps to keep his long tail from wagging too conspicuously inside his trousers, — that is supposing he possessed such an unearthly embellishment.

"I'll tell you what we want," he at last chuckled, with the air of a man who is about to utter a devilish good joke. "We want, first, a bill to stop the collection of interest until the loan falls due, when we will pay the one hundred and thirty millions at once, if we can. Second, we want a bill to change the government lien from a first to a second mortgage, so that we can issue a batch of first-mortgage bonds and raise money for current expenses. That's all we want now, Vane, and I'm sure it's moderate."

"O, ain't it, though?" grinned Honest John, half indignant and half amused at this impudent rapacity. "I'm sure it's very kind of you not to ask Uncle Sam to throw in the whole loan as a present. I dare say you might get it."

"O, we're not a bit greedy," Dorman continued to chuckle. "Well, now, to go back to business, we must have good men to help us. We want the very best. The fellows who have pushed us through so far are mainly such notorious deadbeats in point of character that they would throw discredit on a recruiting agency. We want a fresh lot, and a respectable lot. We want such fellows as Christian and Faithful in the Senate, and you and Greatheart and Hopeful in the House."

Honest John Vane pondered; he thought of his good fame, and then he thought of his debts; he thought of his insufficient salary, and of the abounding millions of the Great Subfluvial. Finally he came to the risky decision that he would just ask the way to the bottomless pit, reserving for further consideration the question of leaping into its seething corruption.

"How are you going to get us?" he inquired, in a choked and almost inaudible voice, the voice of a man who is up to his lips in a quicksand.

The eyes of the Mephistopheles of the lobby glowed with a lurid excitement which bore an infernal resemblance to joy. He had a detestable hope that at last he was about to strike a bargain with his simple Faust. There was more than the greed of lucre in his murky countenance; there was seemingly a longing to buy up honesty, character, and self-respect; there was eagerness to purchase a soul.

"We can make things just as pleasant as a financier could want," he answered, coming at once to the point of remuneration. "You don't want stock in the Subfluvial, of course. If you held shares in that and then gave it a lift, the opposition lobby would bawl about it, and the public might impute selfish motives. But we have got up an inside machine, which is all the same with the Subfluvial, and yet isn't the same. It works under a separate charter, and yet has the same engineers. It builds the tunnel, handles the capital once or twice, and keeps what sticks to its fingers. It's a construction committee, in short, which fixes its own compensation. It's a sure, quiet, rich thing for dividends. I don't know a safer or more profitable investment. We can let you into that, and you can draw your hundred and fifty per cent a year, and all the while be as snug as a bug in a rug. Will you come inside the rug? Will you stand by the great, sublime, beneficent, liberal Subfluvial? Say you will, John! It's a noble national enterprise. Say you'll see it out."

As Honest John Vane stared at his grimy tempter, striving to decide whether he would accept or spurn that tempter's degrading proffer, he had the air of a man who is uncomfortably ill, and his appearance was matched by his sensations. There was a woful sickness in his heart; and, to use a common phrase more easily understood than explained, it struck to his stomach; and that fleshly-minded organ, taking its own physical view of the matter, electrified every nerve with the depressing thrills of bodily indisposition. He was as ill at ease and as pale as the unseaworthy landsman whom Neptune has just begun to toss in his great blanket. Moreover, he *felt* that he was pale; he knew that he did not present the healthy countenance of stalwart innocence; and this knowledge increased his discomposure, and made him look fairly abject.

It would be impossible, short of reiterating all the circumstances of our story, to give a complete idea of his thoughts and emotions. But we must specify that he sorrowfully blamed his wife for those follies of hers which had driven him into debt; that he cursed the widespread social extravagance which had made of that wife a pitiless, or at least an uncomprehending extortioner and spendthrift; and that he cursed even more bitterly that whole system of subsidies and special legislation which was now drawing around him its gilded nets of bribery. There were stinging reminiscences, too, of his worthy glorying in the title of Honest; of his loud and sincere promises to acclaiming fellow-citizens that he would labor tirelessly at the task of congressional reform; of his noble trust that he might establish a broad and permanent fame on the basis of official uprightness. All these things went through him at once like a charge of small shot. No wonder that his moral nature bled exhaustively, and that he had the visage of a man stricken with mortal wounds.

It must be observed, however, that his grief and compunction were not of the highest character, such as would doubtless accompany the downfall of a truly noble nature. There is a rabble in morals as well as in manners, and to this spiritual mobocracy Vane belonged by birth. The fibre of his soul was coarse, and it had never been refined or purified by good breeding, and very likely it was not capable of taking a finish. No such "self-made man" was he as Abraham Lincoln, or many another who has shed honor on lowly beginnings, and made the phrase "self-made" dear to millions. On the contrary, he was one of those whose mission it is to show the millions that they are disposed to over-estimate the qualities implied by this absurdly popular epithet. He had his good fruits;

but they sprang from feeble or selfish motives, and so were not likely to bear abundantly. He did not prize virtue for its own sake, but because the name of it had brought him honor. In truth, his far-famed honesty had thus far stood on a basis of decent egotism and respectable vanity. When his self-conceit was sapped by debt and by the sense of legislative failure, the superstructure sagged, leaned, gaped in rifts, and was ready to sink under the first deluge of temptation.

In the expression with which he looked at Dorman, you could see how much his vanity was hurt. He had a stare of dislike and anger which would have caused a human being of ordinary sensibilities either to quit the room or roll up his sleeves for a fight. Like many another over-tempted person, he hated his tempter while submitting to him, and because he submitted to him. His soul, indeed, was in a confounding turmoil of contradictions, and did not work at all as the souls of accountable creatures are meant to work. Had he retained full presence of mind, he would have held back his concession to wrong until he could make a bargain, and sell his soul for at least what little it was worth. But his very first words of sin were at once an apology for it and a confession that he was not in circumstances to dictate his own price for it.

"Darius, I am awfully hard up," he said, with an abject pathos which ought to have drawn a bonus from the most griping and illiberal of the Lords of Hell.

But an utterance of weakness or suffering was the last thing in the world which could draw generosity from the nondescript sinner who had come to entice him. It may be that Dorman was only a fiend in embryo, who was still awaiting diabolical regeneration, and had not even

171

commenced his growth in the true infernal graces; but if so, he was a chrysalis or tadpole of truly abominable promise, whose evolution would be likely to fill all Gehenna with gladness, and cause it to welcome his coming with strewings of its most sulphurous palm-branches. No doubt his anthropological experience had been an advantage to him; he had absorbed all the evil that he could find in business, politics, and lobbying; he had developed to the utmost the selfish, pitiless instincts of traffic and chicane. All the law and the prophets that he knew were comprised in the single Mammonite commandment, Thou shalt buy cheap and sell dear.

The consequence was that he listened to John Vane's avowal of bankruptcy without a throb of compassion. Indeed, his only emotion on hearing that cry of a stumbling soul was a huckstering joy in the hope of getting a good thing at a bargain. The cheaper the better, the more of a trading triumph, and therefore the nobler. Whoever has read the stories of those diabolical temptations which were so common in the "ages of faith," knows that Satan is anxious to purchase immortal spirits on the shabbiest possible terms. The reason is plain: a beggarly price not only "bears" the market, but throws contempt on the "line of merchandise" traded for; it exposes to the scorn of chaos the spiritual and, therefore, most perfect work of the Creator.

16

DORMAN possessed in full measure the Luciferian humor of higgling.

Discovering that Vane was in financial extremities, he inferred that he would "sell out at a low figure." He had come empowered to offer five thousand dollars for the respectability which lay in Honest John's character; but he now decided that he would throw out only the bait with which he was accustomed to angle for the ordinary fry of Congressmen. If one thousand dollars' worth of stock sufficed to land his fish, there would remain four thousand dollars for himself, a very fair commission.

"You ought not to miss this chance, Vane," he said, with the calmness of a horsedealer. "We will guarantee you ten per cent, and it is pretty certain to pay fifty, and may pay twice as much."

"Of course it will pay anything that you inside fellows choose to make it pay," answered the Congressman, with a bluntness which revealed his moral inflammation. He was in the condition of a man who is having a tooth pulled, and who cannot but desire to make a bite at his dentist's fingers.

"Well, that's so, of course," admitted Dorman, with the smile of a trickster who decides to make a merit of enforced frankness. "But it wouldn't do for us to cut the profits too fat, you know. We can't divide up the whole Subfluvial stock and government loan among the construction ring. We've got to draw a line somewhere. Say a hundred per cent, now."

"Say so, if you like," returned John Vane, sullenly, meanwhile searching in vain for some pecuniary escape from this bargain, so full of risk for his good name and of humiliation to his vanity.

"Well, I say so; that's agreed on," winked Dorman.

There was a silence now which endured through several eternal seconds. The statesman who was for sale and the lobbyist who wanted to buy him were both alike unwilling to name a price, the former through shame and the latter through niggardliness.

"There isn't much of this left," Dorman at last resumed. "Stands at one or two hundred per cent above par. It's such a safe and paying thing that there's been a loud call for it."

Vane made no response. He had an appearance even of not listening to the agent of the abysses of corruption. The truth is that he was beginning to recover his self-possession, and with it his faculty for dickering.

"I could let you have five hundred of it, though," continued the lobbyist, still bent upon getting his soul for a song.

"Do you mean to insult me?" demanded Vane, with a glare which might mean either huckstering anger at the meanness of the bribe or virtuous indignation at being offered a bribe at all.

"Say a thousand, then," added Dorman, with a spasmodic start, as if the offer had been jerked out of him by red-hot pincers, or as if the breath in which he uttered

174

it had been a scalding steam of brimstone. "Senators Christian and Faithful took a thousand each, and were glad to get it. Let me see; we've had to go as high as that on some of the House fellows, too, — such men as Greatheart and Hopeful, for instance. Well, I ought not to mention names."

"Why, those are our biggest figure-heads!" Vane almost shouted, springing up and pacing the room in amazement.

"Of course they are," grinned Dorman. "The very highest sign-boards in Congress, the saints and the advocates of reform, and the watch-dogs of the Treasury! There are no men of better reputation inside politics."

"I wouldn't have thought it — of *them*," pursued Vane. "I knew there was a raft of fellows who took investments in things that they voted for. But I supposed there were *some* exceptions."

The lobbyist knew that there were exceptions; he had learned by dint of rebuffs that Congressmen existed who were either pure enough or rich enough to be above pecuniary temptation; but he was careful not to mention this fact to his proposed victim.

"Well, you see how it is, at last," he resumed. "You see that the candle of fame only lights up a game for money, and now what's the use of your holding different notions from everybody else? You haven't been practical, John Vane; you've been eccentric and highfalutin. I put it to you, as one fair-minded business man to another, is it generous or just for a capitalist to ask a member to work for him gratis? I say not. If I see an honest chance to make five thousand dollars, and you give me a lift which enables me to use that chance, I ought to allow you a share in the investment. And that's what I do. I've got five thousand dollars of this inside stock——"

Here he had another spasmodic start, which ended in a prolonged fit of coughing, as though the brimstone fumes which we have imputed to his breath were unusually dense and stifling. Of course it could not have been remorse or shame which interfered with his breathing, although the five thousand dollars which he talked of had been given him to transfer to Vane, and although his own private share of the "Hen Persuader" stock already amounted to fifty thousand. Of remorse or shame he must have been fundamentally incapable. If he felt any human passion at this moment, it must have been a peanut peddler's gladness.

"And I offer you twenty per cent of it," he continued, when he had recovered his utterance. "That's about fair, I think, for I've only this one investment on hand, and can't possibly attend to more, while you can dip into all the national enterprises that are going. And don't you make Puritanic faces over it. It isn't money, you see. So help me Lucifer! I wouldn't think of offering money to you. It's just a business chance. Is there anything low in a Congressman's putting his money where his constituents put theirs? Isn't he thereby joining his fortunes with theirs? That's what I said to Greatheart and he couldn't get round it, and he took the stock."

"I'll — I'll take it, too," was John Vane's response, — a mere choked gasp of a response, but heard, perhaps, all through Pandemonium.

"All right!" laughed Dorman, leaping up and giving his member's back a slap, which ought to have left the imprint of a fiery hand. "Well, I'll hold the stock for you," he promptly added, with a sly sparkle in his smoky eyes. "Just to keep your name off the books and out of the newspapers, you understand."

176

Our Congressman pondered a full minute before he replied. He was no longer Honest John Vane, but he desired to remain such in the eyes of the public, and consequently he did not want the stock in his own name. At the same time he shrewdly doubted whether it would be worth much to him, if it stood to the credit of Dorman. His countenance was at this moment a study for a painter of character. There were two phases in it, the one growing and the other waning, like the new moon encroaching upon the old. In a moment you might say that it had undergone a transfiguration, though not such a one as apostles would desire to honor with tabernacles. All the guile in his soul — that slow, loutish guile which lies at the bottom of so many low-bred and seemingly simple natures — rose to the surface of his usually genial and hearty expression, like oily scum to the surface of water. His visage actually took a physical lubricity from it, and shone like the fraudful superficies of a shaved and greased pig.

"I won't trouble you to hold my property for me, Darius," he said. "I'll hold it in my own name. Honesty is the best policy."

This last phrase was a noteworthy one. It showed that he had already entered upon the life of a hypocrite. A little before he had been a living body of honesty; now he was a vampire, but he still retained his decent carcass.

"Now, — look here, John, — *would* you?" hesitated the lobbyist, who had hoped to make the shares stick to his own fingers. "Christian and Greatheart and those fellows haven't. You see, if there should be an exposure, and this stock should be found in your name, you wouldn't be on the investigating committee."

"Never mind, I'll do the square thing," replied Vane,

to whom it had suddenly occurred that the Great Sub-fluvial and its "Hen Persuader" worked under separate charters, so that a man who held property in one might plausibly claim a right to vote on the other.

"O, well, if you insist upon it," assented Dorman, much chagrined. "If you choose to risk it, why, of course — Well, now about paying for the stock; as you are hard up, suppose we let the dividends go towards that."

"Suppose we don't," promptly returned Vane, remembering how direly he needed ready cash. "Suppose you hand me the certificates at once, and the dividends as fast as they fall in."

The lobbyist looked at his victim with an air of spite qualified by admiration. Maelzel might have had a similar expression (though not by any possibility so vicious and diabolical) when he was beaten at chess by his own automaton.

"I have caught a Tartar," he grinned. "When you turn your attention to finance, John, you show your business training. Your game isn't the safest, though. All the sly old hands, — all the fellows who have graduated in the lobbies of the State Legislatures, and bribed their way from there into Congress, — all those shysters have had the shares sold for them and taken nothing but the plain greenbacks. I see what your false bosom is made of, John, — the fair front of honest simplicity and ignorance. It may do you, and it may not. The faster a hog swims the more he cuts his throat with his own hoofs," he added, with a spite which made him coarse. "You'd better let me keep the stock for you."

"Well," sighed the imp, who had not bought a soul as cheaply as he had hoped, "have it your own way, then. I'll bring the certificate to-morrow."

17

AND now Honest John Vane had become Dishonest John Vane, and justified Dorman's contemptuous nickname of Weathercock John.

He had accepted stock in a financial enterprise, which might fairly be called a Juggernaut of swindling, on the understanding that he would grease its rusted wheels with fresh legislation, and help roll it once more through the public treasury and over the purses of the people.

In so doing, he had trampled on such simian instincts of good as had been born in him, on such development of conscience as he had been favored with during his sojourn in this christianly human cycle, on resolutions which he knew to be noble, because everybody had told him so, and on promises whereby he had secured power. He had proved that, so far as he could be a moral anything, he was a moral failure. In all the miscellaneous "depravity of inanimate things," he most resembled a weak-jointed pair of tongs, such as pusillanimously cross their legs, let their burdens drop back into the coals, and pinch the hand which trusts them.

In short, he had easily fallen into the loose horde of Congressional foragers or "bummers," who never do one stroke of fighting in the battle of real statesmanship, but prowl after plunder in the trail of the guerillas of the lobby. Their usual history, as the well-informed Darius Dorman has already hinted to us, was this: they had acquired a mastery of log-rolling and bribery and stealing in the halls or the lobbies of the State Legislatures; and, having there gained sufficient wealth or influence, had bribed their way to Congress, with the sole object of plundering more abundantly. John Vane, on the contrary, had been elected by a hopeful people, going about with a lantern to look for an honest politician. He had meant to be honest; he had, so to speak, taken upon himself the vows of honesty; and now, for a thousand or two of dollars, he had broken them. He differed from a majority of his brethren in piratical legislation just as a backslider and hypocrite differs from a consistent sinner.

Can we palliate his guilt? We repeat here, — for the moral importance of the fact will justify iteration, — that he came of a low genus. It was a saying of the oldest inhabitant of Slowburgh, that "up to John's time there never had been a magnificent Vane." No more was there one now. Although some blessed mixture had clarified the family soul in him a little, he still retained much sediment deposited by the muddy instincts of his ancestors, and a very little shaking stirred it all through his conduct. Proper breeding and education might have made him a permanently worthy soul; but of those purifying elements he had been favored with only a few drops. He had risen somewhat above his starting-point, but he still remained below the highest tide-water mark of vice, and got no foothold on the dry land of the loftier moral motives. Sidling crab-like about in these low grounds, the daily flood rolled in and submerged him.

It is impossible to insist too strongly upon the fact that he had no sound self-respect and lofty sense of honor.

Of that noble pride which renders unassailable the integrity of a Washington, a Calhoun, an Adams, or a Sumner, he had not laid the lowest foundation, and perhaps could not. In place of this fortress, he possessed only the little, combustible block-house of vanity. All, or nearly all, his uprightness had sprung from a desire to win the hurrahs of men who were no better than himself, or who were his inferiors. The title of Honest John (knocked down to him at such a shamefully low price as must have given him but a slight idea of its value) had merely tickled his conceit, as red housings tickle that of a horse. It was a fine ornament, which distinguished him from the mass of John Vanes, some of whom were in jail. It was a *nom de guerre*, by aid of which he could rally voters around him, and perhaps win further glories at the polls. Mainly for these trivial and merely external reasons had he striven to hold on to it, and not because he believed that reputation, self-respect, and sense of honor were precious, far more precious than happiness or even life.

Such a motive force is of course no force at all, but a mere weathercock, which obeys the wind of public opinion, instead of directing it. Vane had now been exposed for some time to a moral breath which differed greatly from that of his hard-working, precise, exact, and generally upright constituents. In the first place, he had found, as he thought, that in Washington his title of Honest brought him no influence and little respect. He suspected that it was chiefly his unwillingness to have a finger in the fat pies of special legislation which had caused him to be kept on the minor committees. He saw other members, who were as new, as untrained, and as comically ignorant as himself, — but who had the fame among the lobbyists of being "good workers," and able to "put things through," — he saw them called to positions of distinguished responsibility, far higher on the roll of honor than himself. He learned, or supposed he had learned, that many Congressmen kept Uncle Sam's eagle setting on their own financial eggs. He knew members who had come to Washington poor, and who now owned square miles on the lines of great railroads, and rode in their carriages, while he and his wife walked. For a time, the prosperity of these knaves had not punctured his soap-bubble honesty, because he still believed that there was a Congressional public which condemned them and respected him. Classing himself with Senators Christian and Faithful, and with those almost equally venerated images, Representatives Greatheart and Hopeful, he continued for a time to stand proudly in his honored niche, and to despise the rabble of money-changers below.

But at last Dorman had told him, and his necessities easily led him to believe, that he was alone in his virtuous poverty; Christian, Greatheart, and the other reputed temples of righteousness, were nothing but whited sepulchres, full of railroad bonds and all uncleanness. This illumination from the secrets of the pit bewildered him, and caused him to topple from the narrow footing of his probity. He resolved that he would not be the only case of honest indigence and suffering in the whole political world. Besides, what risk did he run of losing his home popularity by accepting a few golden eggs from the manipulators of the Hen Persuader? The fact might become current news in Hell, but it would never reach Slowburgh. Was it likely that Congress would expose the interior of a thieving machine on which so many of its members had left their finger-marks? Even if an investigation should be forced, there was such a trick as doing it with closed doors, and there was such a material as committee-room whitewash.

There was still a momentous question before Vane, — the question whether he would continue to walk with the Mammonite crew, or make use of his deliverance from debt to resume his former respectable courses. The manner in which he decided it furnishes another proof of the jelly-fish flabbiness which characterized his rudimentary nature. Many a cultivated spirit tumbles once down the declivity of guilt, and then climbs back remorsefully to the difficult steeps of well-doing. But our self-manufactured and self-instructed hero continued to stick in the mud where he had drifted, like any other mollusk, and absorbed and fattened and filled his shell, a model of stolid and immoral content.

Just in one direction — the only direction in which he had been thoroughly educated — he showed energy. At business he had worked hard and made himself what is called a good business man, sharp-sighted in detecting his own interest, and vigorous in delving for it. If in the present case he had not made a particularly fine bargain for himself, it had been because he was new to that thieves' brokerage, the lobby, and bewildered at finding himself hustled into it. But, although he had sold his virtue at a low figure, he was now determined to get the full price agreed upon. As Dorman did not bring him the promised certificate of stock, he sought him out and secured it. Next he heard that a dividend had fallen due on the day of his purchase; hence another call on his fellow-sinner, and a resolute demand for the sum total of said dividend.

"But the transfer is dated the day after the dividend," objected Dorman, who like the rest of his subterranean kind, did not want to pay a cent more for a soul than he could help.

"Yes, I know it is," answered Dishonest John Vane, angrily. "And that's a pretty trick to play on a man whose help you ask for. Now I want you to make that transfer over again, and date it the day on which I took the stock, and pay me the dividend due on it."

Dorman, wizened with disappointed greed and slyness, looked less like a triumphant goblin than usual, and more like a scorched monkey. His wilted visage twitched, his small, quick, vicious eyes glanced here and there anxiously, and he had an air of being ready to drop on all fours and scramble under a table. Nevertheless, as there was no resisting a lawgiver of the United States, he corrected the certificate and paid the dividend.

"I don't see how I came to make this blunder," he chattered, arching his eyebrows as apologetical monkeys do.

"You don't pronounce it right; it wasn't blunder, but plunder," smiled Vane, with a satirical severity, suggestive of Satan rebuking Sin.

IN an amazingly short time after these solvent providences had befallen Weathercock John, all the lobbyists out of Gehenna seemed to have learned that he was "approachable."

These turkey buzzards have a marvelous aptitude at scenting a moral carcass, and Vane, who did not so much as suspect that he was dead, must have been already in need of burial, and pungently attractive to their abominable olfactories. They gathered around him and settled upon him, until he might be described as fairly black with them. Gentlemen who, to be in character, ought to have had raw necks and a sore-toed gait, croaked into his ears every imaginable scheme for pilfering, not only the fatness and the life-blood, but the very bones out of Uncle Sam. It is arithmetically certain that, had every one of these pick-purse plans been carried out successfully, the Secretary of the Treasury would have had to suspend all manner of payments.

Among so many golden bows of promise, Weathercock John was able to make a judicious pick, and to find lots of full purses at the ends of them. He would have nothing to do with "national highways," because he was already highwaying it on the line of the Great Subfluvial, and did not want to become known as one of the "railroad ring."

He selected the congenial case of a deceased horse, who had been killed by our troops in Western New York during the war of 1812, and who had already drawn his ghostly claim for damages through five Congresses, the amount thereof quadrupling with every successive journey, so that it had risen from $125 to $32,000.

Also he pitched upon the case of certain plantation buildings in Florida, which had been destroyed by the same indiscreet soldiery while striving to defend them from the Seminoles, or by the Seminoles while struggling to take them from the soldiery; and which, by dint of repeated "settlements and adjustments on principles of justice and equity," every settlement being made the pretext of a new adjustment, and every adjustment the pretext of a new settlement, had grown in worth from about $8,000 to about $134,000, — one of the most remarkable instances of the rise of property ever witnessed in a thinly settled country.

Likewise he hit upon the grievance of a mail contractor, who, having failed to carry his mails and so forfeited his contract, now demanded (through his heirs) $10,000 in damages; also $15,000 for mail services, in addition to those not rendered; also $20,000 of increased compensation for the mail services not rendered, together with interest and costs to the amount of $15,000 more.

These and some dozen other similar swindles, our member took under his legislative protection, proposing to put them through as such little jokers usually are put through; that is, by tacking them on to appropriation bills at the very end of the session. As for remuneration, he was fair minded enough to be content with ten per cent on each successful claim, whereas some unscrupulous statesmen extorted as much as fifteen or twenty. It is needless to say that, in view of this conscientious moderation, the lobby itself was stricken with a sense of unholy gratitude, and began to shout through its organs, "Hurrah for Honest John Vane!" You may imagine how it delighted and strengthened him to find that, no matter what villainous trick he played upon the public, he could not lose his glorious nickname. So cheered was he by this incongruous good fortune that he ventured to introduce a little bill of his own into Congress, appropriating $50,000 for a new cemetery for "the heroic dead of the late war," the contract for the coffins to be awarded to one Elnathan Sly, who was his own man of straw or *alter ego*.

Meantime he would have nothing to do with those visionary projects which "had no money in them." His motto was, "No Irish need apply," meaning thereby indigent applicants for legislation, or applicants who would not offer to go snacks. When an author urged him to introduce an international copyright bill, he cut short his visitor's prosing about the interests of literature by saying brusquely, "Sir, I may as well tell you at once that I don't care anything about this subject, and I don't believe anybody can make me care about it." When some simple college professors wanted him to propose an appropriation for the observation of an eclipse, he got rid of the venerable Dryasdusts by a stroke of rare humor, telling them that his specialty was Revolutionary pensions. When a wooden-legged captain of volunteers applied to him for the Slowburgh Post-Office, he treated him with promises, which sent him home promptly in high spirits, and then secured the position for one of his own wire-pullers, a man who had enlisted for the war in the Home Guards.

A great change, you will say; an unnaturally sudden eclipse; an improbably complete decadence. Not so; in his inmost being Vane had not altered; only in the incrustations of life deposited by surroundings. Barring the molluscous characteristics of easy good nature, and that sort of companionable generosity which amounts to give and take, he had never been beneficent and unselfish. He had not moral sympathy enough to feel the beauty of virtue in the individual, nor intellect enough to discover the necessity of virtue to the prosperity of society, nor culture enough to value any educational instrument finer than a common school. Considering the bare poverty of his spiritual part, indeed, our Congressman was merely a beggar on horseback; and it was no wonder that, once temptation got him faced hellwards, he rode to the devil with astonishing rapidity.

Well, John Vane fell from respectable indigence into degradingly thrifty circumstances. He paid all the debts which he had incurred during his abnormal, or at least accidental, course of honesty, and knew no more what it was to be without a comforting roll of pilfered greenbacks in his pocket. He hired a fine carriage for his wife, and gave her all the funds that she needed for entertainments and shopping, thereby arousing in her fresh respect and affection. Indeed, he so far satisfied the pecuniary expectations of Olympia that she no longer found the wealthy Ironman necessary to her happiness, and fell into a prudent way of discouraging his attentions. Once more our member's home was tranquil, and he happy and glorious in the midst of it. A man who can dazzle and fascinate his own wedded Danaë with showers of gold is nothing less than a Jove of a husband.

It is worth noting that Olympia had no scruples about using these unaccustomed riches, and never once asked where they came from. Had she learned that they were filched from the public treasury, would she have accepted and spent them the less freely? A venerable Congressman, thoroughly versed in all the male and female wickedness of Washington, assures me that women are conscienceless plunderers of public property, and will steal any official article which they can lay hands on, from a paper-folder upward.

At last came the end of the session. As is always the case, it was a season of wild turmoil and uproar, by no means resembling one's idea of legislation, but more like a dam breaking away. The House was as frantic with excitement and as noisy with dissonant speaking as was the tower of Babel after the confusion of tongues. Honorable members who had special bills to push were particularly active and sonorous. They spouted; they tacked on amendments; they electioneered among their brother lawgivers; they were incredibly greedy and shameless. An imaginative observer might have fancied himself in a huge mock-auction shop, with two or three score of impudent Peter Funks hammering away at once, while dead horses were knocked down at a hundred times the price of live ones, and burnt barns, empty cotton bags, rotten steamers, and unbuilt railroads went at similar swindling prices, the victimized purchaser in every case being a rich simpleton called Uncle Sam. The time, talents, and parliamentary skill of the honest members were nearly all used up in detecting and heading off the immortal steeds which were turned into the national pastures by the dishonest ones. Many measures of justice, of governmental reform, and even of departmental necessity were, perforce, overlooked and left untouched. It seemed as though the only thing which Congress was not under obligation to attend to was the making of laws for the benefit of the whole people.

In this raid of special legislation upon real legislation John Vane was one of the most active and adroit guerillas. His "genial" smile simpered from desk to desk, like Hector's shield blazing along the ranks of Trojan war. He had never smiled so before; he very nearly smiled himself sick; he proved himself the smiler of smilers. There was no resisting such an obviously warm-hearted fellow, especially as he was generous, too, offering to vote as he would be voted for. And everything prospered with him; the taxes gathered from his countrymen melted on his schemes like butter on hot pancakes; and when he left the House at midnight he was a man in "respectable circumstances."

He now had funds enough to carry the next nominating caucus in his district, and thus, with Dorman's potent aid, to make fairly sure of a return to Congress. As he had once swept the ballot-boxes as Honest John Vane, so he purposed to sweep them again as Dishonest John Vane. But is the golden calf of lobbydom to be the directing deity of our politics forever? Is no axe to be laid to the root of this green bay tree of Slowburgh? We shall see.

WHAT were the prospects of Weathercock John in the face of that terrible scrutiny of political character, a new election?

He had now served two years in the honorable Congress of the United States, after such a fashion that, could he have had his deserts, he would have served ten more in jail.

But — as the mountain brigands of Greece and the municipal highwaymen of New York can both testify — it is not the custom of some communities to execute justice upon criminals, so long as injustice is procurable for love or money. Moreover, our ignominious member had thus far been able to keep that cardinal eleventh commandment, "Thou shalt not be found out." He was still worshiped by the simple and lowly masses of his district as Honest John Vane; and, furthermore, he had store of that golden oil which is one of the best of all lubricators for the wheels of political fortune.

Thus, instead of going to the tread-mill and becoming an object of reverential pity to sentimental philanthropists, he went into a canvass for re-election at the head of a faithful flock of baaing adherents, who did not see how he had led them through the brambles of needless taxation, and who were so bewitched with the instinct of following a bellwether that, had they discovered all of Vane's ignorance and rascality, they would not have deserted him. Not that he bought the popular suffrage with money, or could do it. Thanks be to the remaining mercy of Heaven, few freemen as yet sell their votes in Slowburgh. Having no feculent system of special legislation to rot them with its drippings, they are for the most part of sounder morals than the adventurers who contrive to represent them. But there were wire-pullers to be conciliated, oratorical forums to be hired, posters and ballots to be printed, vote-distributors to be paid. Vane's tithes from his relief and subsidy bills covered these expenses nicely, and to the entire satisfaction of an enlightened and moral constituency, fond of economy in national legislation, and boastful of the honesty which a republic is supposed to generate.

Of course he found the franking privilege as useful as if he had never denounced it. He was almost grateful in these campaigning days for the congressional insignificance which had disenabled him from reforming that abuse. A so-called secretary, whom he had left in Washington with several thousand "franks," sold one half of those autographs as his own perquisite, and deluged Vane's field of labor with the other half. Every mechanic in Slowburgh got a report on agriculture, and every farmer got a report on manufactures. The speeches which the so-called secretary had written, and which our member had obtained leave to print in the Congressional Globe without preliminary delivery, fell in such abundant showers throughout the district that it was a wonder they had not been foretold in the almanac. The Washingtonian assistant, by the way, must have been a fellow of some ability; he managed this system of political irrigation not only with vigor, but with judgment. For example, among all the public documents with which he fructified Slowburgh, there was not a single copy of the Report on the Corruption of Members of Congress. It was judicious, certainly; for had we been brought to remember the infamy of Matteson, we might not have been so happy in voting for Vane.

There was, indeed, one ugly week, when it seemed as if the torches of our nocturnal processions burned blue, and we almost feared to look at our candidate lest we should see signs of unworthiness in his face. Certain lobbyists, who had not been able to get what they thought their allowance of eggs out of the Hen Persuader, set afloat vindictive stories to the effect that that wonderful financial machine was nothing but a contrivance to corrupt Congressmen into voting favors to the Great Subfluvial, and that its retaining fees had been pocketed by some of the most famous champions of our party, such as Christian, Greatheart, and Honest John Vane.

These charges were picked up and used for ammunition by a brazen opposition which was as deep in the mud as we were in the mire. Every shot spread consternation through our array. There was danger lest we should set up the Gaulish war-cry of *Nous sommes trahis,* and either flinch from the polls or vote a split ticket. Even the political priesthood of wire-pullers, who stood about Vane as the Scotch Presbyterian elders encompassed Leslie, began to doubt whether it would not be well to make another nomination. But in the end this select and tried synagogue (of Satan?) decided to stick to their candidate and to patch up the rents in his ephod. They began by denying flatly that he owned any Hen Persuader stock, or any other property connected with the Great Subfluvial. Next they set a committee over him to prevent him from avowing such ownership. This committee guarded him all day and put him to bed at night; it went before him like a cloud and behind him like a darkness, keeping him constantly shrouded in non-committalism; it held interviewing reporters at a distance, or whispered evasive answers to their questions. Never was a Grand Lama or a Roi Fainéant more completely secluded. Only a deaf-mute, with all his fingers amputated, could be laid under such a conversational embargo.

This inspired discretion had its reward; various providences arrived to favor it. Good and true men perceived that the whole air was full of "campaign lies," and naturally inferred that this story about the Hen Persuader briberies was one of them. Moreover, it was soon "nailed to the counter" by positive and public letters of denial from Christian, Greatheart, and other implicated seraphim. Of course such men would not prevaricate, we argued, and considered the charges entirely refuted. And now we justified Weathercock John; we imputed his silence to the conscious rectitude of a worthy soul; we said that he had done rightly in treating slander with unresponsive scorn. Thus reassured, we went in a solid phalanx to the polls, and triumphantly sent our special legislator back to Congress.

Nobody was better pleased with the victory than Darius Dorman. It was, by the way, somewhat of a satire upon our human joy that such a "burnt eyed nigger" of the pit, such a mere fieldhand in the earthly plantation of Lucifer, should have shared it. The moment he heard the result he looked up Vane and congratulated him in forms and liturgies of profanity not often heard above ground.

"It is a triumph of the good cause," he continued, with so sarcastic a grin that our heavy-witted member thought him either impertinent or crazy; "and, by the infernal hoofs and horns, the good cause needed it. If we had been beaten, the Great Subfluvial would have been smashed to make way for some other national enterprise. As it is, I think we can keep things white-washed, and perhaps head off an investigation altogether."

"An investigation!" exclaimed Vane, his genial smile falling agape with dismay. "Do you think there will be an investigation?"

"You may bet what soul you have on it," declared the lobbyist. "Just as sure as the party believes those charges to be false, it will demand an overhauling of them, of course, to confound the opposition."

Our Congressman saw the point, and seemed to feel it in his marrow. "If they look this thing up," he gasped, "what's to become of me?"

"I don't know and I don't care," responded Dorman, with a frank brutality which made Vane resolve not to quarrel with him; "what I want to know is, what's to become of me? Here I have all my results and my materials of labor in those two companies. If the Hen Persuader is called on to refund to the Subfluvial, or if the Subfluvial is foreclosed on by the government, I am a poor devil for certain. Well, we are in the same boat; we must pull together. If you won't expose my fashion of doing business, I won't expose your share in the profits of it."

Vane answered in his non-committal fashion; he said nothing, and he did not even look at his guide and ruler in sin; but he gently nodded his assent.

"I always meant to pay you for that stock," he continued, for he was very anxious now to make friends with this Mammon of unrighteousness. "I'll settle with you for it some day, Darius; I'm a little short now. This election, you know."

"O, yes, I know," Dorman grinned epileptically. "It has cost us both a good bit of money. Well, take your time about it; pay me when it comes handy. I can trust your honesty, John, under the circumstances."

The Congressman turned away, full of an inward wrath, but placid, meek, and sleek on the surface, for his tallowy nature did not come easily to an open boil. He was angry at the lobbyist for his sarcasm; he perfectly hated him for that avarice and hardness which would not give a receipt for payment on those shares, without the money; but he must not and would not quarrel with him, so brotherly is the communion of Satan!

FOR once Dorman was correct in a prophecy. The recollection of the "Great Subfluvial slanders" rankled in the soul of an honest and truth-loving nation.

After the election had been carried and the country duly saved from its quadrennial crisis, it seemed just and necessary to put calumny to open shame, and thus rob it of influence in the future. Virtuous constituencies and a press which at least spoke the words of virtue clamored for an investigation which should vindicate the innocence of Christian, Greatheart, and Company, and put their lying accusers in the pillory. "We want justice done you," cheerfully shouted a believing party to its demi-gods, streaming piteously with the rotten eggs of the Hen Persuader.

It was in vain that these revered fetishes whispered to their confidants that justice was precisely what they were afraid of, and interceded with such divinities as they believed in to save them from their friends. In vain did a sadly wise Congress endeavor to amuse and pacify the country by throwing overboard that precious tub of abuses, the franking privilege. In vain did Weathercock John set his daily organ to celebrating and imputing to himself a reform which he had so long promised and which he now so unwillingly conceded. The popular whale took no notice of a plaything which at any other time might have diverted it for years, and continued to thrash the political ocean into foam with its rushings and plungings after investigations.

Amid this commotion John Vane rowed about in his cockle-shell of a character with all the agility that terror can give. He was so accustomed to value himself on being honest that the thought of being publicly condemned as dishonest was almost as dreadful to him as it would have been to an upright soul. So oppressive was his wretchedness that he craved not only help but also sympathy, that favorite consolation of the sorrowful feeble. He was in the spiritual state of certain weak-minded murderers, who cannot sleep of nights until they have told some friend the particulars of their crime. So entirely had the backbone been taken out of him that he could not hold himself erect in the presence of his wife, but wilted upon her slight shoulder for support. It was an abject confession of decrepitude; for he had learned to consider her as totally lacking in practical sense, and there were impatient moments when he thought of her as merely a lively dunce. But now he must have pity, though it came from a peacock.

"I'm afraid there's trouble a brewing for us," he said, one evening, shaking that perplexed head of his which had been the admiration of his constituents, and which certainly looked large enough to hold all the problems of state.

"What's the matter now?" asked Olympia.

She did not think of trouble to the nation, nor of trouble to her husband. The only idea which occurred to her was that perhaps there was a scarcity of money, and she might be called on to give up the honors of house keeping and put on the disgusting humility of lodgings. It was also a little disagreeable to her, this way that John sometimes got into of coming to her with his grievances, and trying to ease his own mind by burdening hers. It was hardly more pleasant than having a dog make a bed for himself on the skirts of one's lilac silk. She possessed in large measure that unsympathy, alleged by some writers to amount to hostility, which certainly does exist to some extent between the sexes. Her world was very different from her husband's world, and she did not much care to have him take an interest in hers, nor did she want at all to worry about his. That the two spheres had any intimate connection she could rarely perceive, except when the masculine one ceased to radiate gold upon the feminine one.

"Well, the matter is this stupid outcry for investigations," sighed John, loosening the cravat about his somewhat pulpy throat, as if fearful lest it should make a hangman's circle there.

"What investigations? Who is to be investigated?" demanded Olympia, who was as ignorant of the whole matter as if she were an inhabitant of some celestial world where investigations were not needed, or of some infernal one where they were of no use.

"Well, it's a secret," the special legislator continued to drawl, talking about his misdeed unwillingly, but unable to stop talking about it. "However, I suppose it'll all be out before long. I thought I might as well prepare your mind for it," he concluded, feebly hoping that she would say something to prepare *his* mind.

"Well, *what* is it?" asked the wife, distinctly foreseeing trouble for herself, and becoming therefore deeply interested.

"O, I thought I told you," answered John, whose scared conscience had been babbling at such a rate that it seemed to him as if he had made audible confession of his whole iniquity. "Well, it's something about this Great Subfluvial Tunnel under the Mississippi, from the Lakes to New Orleans, — great national enterprise, you know. You see, it was a pretty heavy thing for Simon Sharp and the other boss stockholders to carry, and they had to get some additional assistance from Congress, and to do that they gave some of the members stock, — or rather sold it to them," he added, doubting whether he could trust even his wife with all the truth. "Well, some of the newspapers are charging that this is bribery and corruption, and are bawling for an investigation and making a row generally, as though it was anything new, by George!"

"Have *you* got any of the stock?" inquired Olympia. She saw that the subject was a sore one to her husband, but she was not much in the habit of sparing his feelings, and so was able to come promptly and squarely to the point.

"Not much," replied John, loosening his cravat once more. "Only a thousand."

"That isn't much," said the wife, rather scorning him for not having received more. "Why don't you sell it and get it off your hands?"

Vane made no answer. Of course, selling the stock would not hide the fact that he had owned it, nor shield him from ugly questions as to how he came to be possessed of it. But it seemed useless to try to explain this to Olympia, women were so irretrievably dark-minded in business matters.

"Does it pay anything?" she asked, merely guessing

from his silence that the property was profitable, and that therefore he did not wish to part with it.

"About fifteen hundred a year," confessed the husband, with a sheepish air; "or maybe two thousand."

"Two thousand!" exclaimed the modern Portia, who, as a legislator, was even more "self-taught" than her husband, and consequently more unscrupulous. "Why, you mustn't think of selling it."

The statesman gazed at his privy counsellor in despair. She could not grasp the situation, and he might have known that she could not. To appeal to such a woman for advice and consolation in great trouble was much as if a drowning man should trust to a raft made of millinery.

"It's all very well to talk that way, as though it was as easy as A B C," he answered, quite out of patience with the straw which he had clutched at to so little purpose. "But supposing this costs me my seat? Supposing I get expelled for it? Then you'll understand, I reckon, that it *is* of some consequence, and not so very handy to manage."

Olympia perceived that dulness was imputed unto her, and she felt very angry at the injustice. She knew that she was not dull; nobody ever hinted such an idea but her husband; other men complimented her for her cleverness, her social powers, etc.

"Then what did you get yourself in such a scrape for?" she retorted sharply. "You needn't blame *me* for it; I didn't do it."

"Yes, you did," insisted John, and with much truth. "I got into this very scrape to raise money for your house keeping and receptions and carriages and all those other confounded ruinous things that you could have got along just as well without. And, by George, the whole fol-de-rol nonsense has got to stop!" he exclaimed, his long-continued excitement over the threatened investigation bursting up in an explosion of domestic wrath. "We don't keep house this session. And we don't stay here at the Arlington, neither. We go back to a boarding-house; and we go to parties afoot, too. The omnibus ain't running this session," he added, with a bitterly jocose allusion to "omnibus bills," and their profitable loads of special enactments. "Shoe-leather will have to do our traveling. It's all the turn-out that I can pay for."

Of course there was a scene. Of course Olympia did not surrender her woman's right to luxury without a tearful and little less than hysterical struggle. But John Vane, rendered pitiless by terror concerning his political future, was for once master over his own household. He made arrangements that very day for leaving his fine rooms in the Arlington and going into lodgings. At first sight, his economy seems unnecessarily hard, in view of the fact that he still had several thousand dollars left out of the illegal gleanings of the last session, and thus was a richer man than when he first came to Washington. But this money had gone into the purchase of a new patent in refrigerators, and he could not realize on it without sacrificing a very promising business chance. Moreover, he saw that in the present public excitement about "jobbing" legislation, he must forego its emoluments for a time, and thus diminish his income. Finally, it seemed to be absolutely necessary to put on the guise of poverty, if he cared to preserve his repute for honesty. All these things he explained to Olympia, in a discreetly vague way, remembering the while that she might be just goose enough to go and cackle it abroad, but anxious, nevertheless, to make her contented with him.

"You see, we *have* been going it rather strong on style," he added. "Ten thousand dollars a year is a pretty tall figure for four persons, two of 'em children. I suppose we got into that way because other people set the example," he concluded, not wishing to be hard on his wife.

"If we could only have the rooms on the first floor, I could stand it — for a while," was the response of the insatiable Olympia, a pathetic tear fringing her long and really lovely eyelashes. "They are only fifteen dollars a month more, and then we would have a nice parlor, or at least a decent one."

"That means dinners, I s'pose," grinned Vane, testily. "Big dinners and little receptions."

"Do you want to shut me out of the world altogether?" was the desperate cry of this persecuted wife.

"Now look here: I *would* do it, — I would if I could," groaned the weak monster of a husband. "If I had a thousand dollars of capital loose, I'd spend it that way, or any way to please you."

"Why don't you borrow?" was the suggestion of a help-meet whose ideas of a loan did not extend so far as the repayment. "I'm sure I have gentlemen friends who would be willing to lend you something."

Although she said "friends," she was thinking of Senator Ironman, and her husband easily divined it. Should he be angry at the suggestion and reject it with self-respectful scorn? Well, he was not so sensitive as he had been when he came to Washington; somehow or other he did not care so much about the look of things and the name of things; on the whole, he could not feel indignation, or at least none to speak of. Indeed, his disintegration of moral sentiments had gone farther than that stage of indifference which simply allows things to take their own course. After meditating for some time over his wife's advice to borrow of her friends, he decided to follow it.

"It would be better to let Ironman lend me the money than to run the chance of his lending it to her," he reasoned. "And then I can tell him that I am hard up, and give him a hint to let other people know it. By George, it's a queer position for an old business man to be in," he added with a mixture of chagrin and amusement; "I never thought once that I should come to want to be considered bankrupt."

21

WHEN the Honorable Mr. Vane was shown into Senator Ironman's library, his usually pink face wore that pallor which anxieties will bring, especially when they are accompanied by discontent with one's self.

The equally pink, though bony and narrow visage of the senator also lost some of its natural color as he advanced to welcome his visitor. It was, by Jove, very queer, he thought, that Vane should drop in at that time of day, just after a fellow's breakfast, as though he were an intimate friend. The two men, we must understand, were not fundamentally fond of each other, as is often the case with two men who admire the same lady.

"I don't altogether fancy Vane," the senator had confessed to his familiars. "Now Mrs. Vane is a magnificent creature, thoroughly well bred and well educated — that is, enough so for society, you understand, — a whole-souled, splendid, dazzling woman, and — and as jolly as possible. She is a woman that shows well in a dance or anywhere. By Jove, she's a stunner, that woman is. I don't know another lady in Washington that could wear crimson roses in her hair without looking faded. She becomes a bouquet superbly, and, by Jove,

I love to give them to her, — she shows one off so! But Vane is another sort of animal altogether. He is rather — rather — in fact, rather *dull*," judged the great man, hitting on the right word at last. "And just a little low, too," he added. "Don't always speak the best grammar. One of your heavy, self-taught men," he explained, forgetting that his own father had begun life as an hostler. "Low man on the whole; in some points, *very* low — and *dull*."

So you perceive he did not admire his visitor, not as much as Slowburgh would have expected. But there were other causes for the Dundreary perplexity which now winked from his pale eyes and crisped his limited forehead. He had noted Vane's unusual ghastliness, and the circumstance alarmed him. What had the man got on his low and dull mind? Was he going to say anything disagreeable about the Ironman bouquets and carriage-drives and other marks of esteem accorded to Mrs. Vane. The senator was so eager and hurried in his expressions of amity and welcome that he fairly stuttered.

"Mr. Ironman, I just dropped in to talk about this Great Subfluvial row," commenced our member in a slightly paralytic voice, for he was at least as much agitated as his host.

"O, — O, indeed!" answered the relieved dignitary of the upper house. "Sit down, sit down," he went on, smiling as cheerily as if the subject were an entirely delightful one. "Had your breakfast? Just as lieve order you up something as not. Say a devilled kidney, now. Well, take a glass of sauterne, then, or a cigar," he urged, forgetting that John was a tee-totaler and a non-smoker.

"I don't use either, thank you," said Vane, holding on to what habits of virtue he had left, though he wanted a glass of wine sadly. "Well, — about this affair, now: do you think there'll be an investigation?"

"Yes, O, yes; *such* a row about it, you know; can't help coming to one; bad for those fellows that are in it," prattled the senator, either forgetting that the bulk of his own fortune had come out of the lobby, or remembering with satisfaction that it had been harvested years ago.

"With closed doors, I s'pose," hoped Dishonest John.

"Don't know about that, by Jove!" and Ironman shook his statesmanlike head. "You see we don't *want* them open; but now and then we have to give in to the newspaper fellows; there's *such* a row about it, you know! I'm afraid some fellows have got to go overboard," he added, much consoled by the thought that the fellows in question would be out of his way. "You see, when a man is found out, it's bad for him."

"Well," sighed Vane, after a long silence, "*I* may have to quit Washington, then."

The senator opened his eyes. So Honest John Vane was "in it," was he? It was curious, by Jove! and he wondered he hadn't thought of it before, and then wondered how it was that all those honest fellows ended so badly. But these ideas were almost immediately chased out of the confined boundaries of his mind by the reflection that, if Vane left Washington, his wife would go too.

"By Jove, that's bad," he broke out. "By Jove, that won't do. We can't spare you and Mrs. Vane. My wife won't know what to do," he explained, "if she loses Mrs. Vane."

The heart of Mrs. Vane's husband grew a little lighter

under these acknowledgments of her importance to the Ironmans.

"Look here! something might be done, you know," continued the senator, thinking harder than he had been accustomed to think since he left school. "I'll run around, myself, among the House fellows, by Jove! I'll ask 'em if something can't be done."

In another instant he had an inspiration. "Look here! Put you on the investigating committee! You needn't investigate your own case, you know. That's it; I'll try to get you put on the investigating committee. It'll help you with the people, — clear up your record; don't you see? And then, if the doors *can* be kept shut, why, you do that, you know. Just the very idea!" he concluded, quite happy over his unexpected attack of shrewdness.

"I'm *afraid*," confessed John Vane, still retaining a little grain of conscience, and rendered timorous by it, "it's a *leetle* too bold for me, — with this stock on my hands."

"I don't see why that should hinder," stared the experienced senator. "Of course you bought the stock, (it's the inside stock, isn't it?) without knowing that it was hitched on to the Great Subfluvial."

"But I haven't paid for it," sighed Vane. "That's the awkward part of the business. And that is partly what I dropped in to see you about," he concluded, his face turning crimson with shame.

"How much?" asked Ironman instantly. He understood that a loan was wanted, and he was willing to make a moderate one; in fact, glad to do it.

"A thousand par," explained our fallen great man.

"O, that's nothing!" laughed the millionnaire, highly amused that Vane should have sold his honesty for so little. "Let me lend you enough to cover it. How much will you have? Say fifteen hundred, now. Here," he continued to laugh, as he went to his safe for the money to hide a bribe, "this trap is always open to a friend. I've had too many good dinners and pleasant evenings at your house not to call you by that name."

"I hope you'll call often," mumbled John Vane in a stifled voice, as he pocketed the greenbacks. "We shall always be delighted to see you."

He felt driven to utter these commonplaces, but he could not return thanks for the loan. He had a bitter feeling or suspicion that he was not under obligations to Ironman, and he was so far from being grateful to him that he positively hated him. It was a satisfaction to him, after he had got into the street, to look back at the house menacingly, and mutter, "You won't see your funds again in one while, old fellow, if you ever do."

This speech of his, by the way, is one of the circumstances of his life from which we can most accurately take his measure in regard to delicacy of feeling and sensitiveness to dishonor.

His next business was to hurry to Dorman's office, and announce that he had come to settle for "that stock."

"What's the damage?" he asked, not at all alluding to the damage which his soul had received.

"How much do you propose to pay?" replied the lobbyist, his smoky eyes giving forth sparks of commingled satire and greed.

"Why, par, of course," said John Vane, a little alarmed. "That's the figure we talked of when I took it."

Dorman skipped about the room and rubbed himself violently, much like a man who discovers that he has a hornet inside his clothes.

"It's been worth three hundred all the while," he exclaimed. "I could have sold it for three hundred the day you got it."

Now Vane could not pay three hundred, nor two hundred, without great inconvenience. Moreover, he was a bargainer born; a bargainer, too, by life-long habit, and valued himself on it. He was as proud of his instinctive, functional, and inevitable dexterity in a dicker as a crab is said to be of walking sideways. So, although he was afraid of Dorman, he resolved to show what he called the spirit of a man, and to resist this low attempt at extortion.

"Look here, Darius, that won't go down," he remonstrated. "The stock may have been worth three hundred once, but it ain't worth it now. People don't want it any more than they want shares in a broken bank with stockholders liable. I'll bet a cookey" (John Vane was not a sporting man, and did not mean to bet anything), "I'll bet a cookey that you can't sell my share, nor anybody's share, for a hundred. But I'll give that for it, because I agreed to and like to stand by my word," he concluded nobly.

"O, very well, anything you like!" grumbled the corruptionist, who saw that he must relinquish his plan for getting back a part of the price which he had paid for a soul.

"And I want a receipt dated back to day of transfer," continued Vane.

"Of course you do," grinned Dorman. "You want it very much indeed. Well, if we give you one, what can you do for us?"

"O, well, I don't know," drawled John, who by this time had caught that easy jog-trot of manner which was his bargaining gait. "You'll need a good deal done for you before the thing is over," he added, picking up the morning Chronicle and pretending to read it. "If I was in the right place," he continued, after a little, "of course I could help you more or less." After a further perusal of the Chronicle, he resumed, "By the way, I met Ironman just now, and he gave me an idea which might work well for you, providing it would work at all."

"Nice fellow, Ironman," smirked Dorman. He guessed immediately that Vane had been drawing on the rich senator for money to pay for the stock; and he wanted to stop him from making use of that resource, for he wanted him poor and in his own power. "Eccentric person in some respects," he went on; "but genial, generous fellow."

Either because there was offence in these remarks, or because this black little creature's breath had some pungent quality, Vane suddenly turned away his head and had a slight spasm of coughing, like a man who had caught a whiff from a lucifer match.

"Yes," he assented presently, looking rather glum. "Well, what was I saying? O, I know (and by the way, this is between us), he suggested putting me on the committee of investigation!"

Dorman laughed so violently that Vane could not help joining him. The peach-blow face of the Congressman turned crimson, and the sombre visage of the lobbyist turned almost black, so apoplectic was their merriment. There was also a sound of other hilarity, not so distinct and therefore all the more singular, about the office. There were faint but audible chuckles in the walls, along the lofty ceiling, and under the floor.

"What's that?" asked Vane, looking about him with

a merely earthly and rather stolid suspicion of eaves-droppers.

"O, nothing that need interrupt us!" smiled Dorman. "This used to be a dwelling-house, and had the name of being haunted. Curious noises about it, you observe; perhaps from subterranean passages to the devil knows where; perhaps nothing but echoes. Well, John, I like your plan. Here is your receipt for payment, dated back to the day of transfer. Give me one thousand; no interest from *you*. We are friends, John, forever," he concluded, with a peculiar accent on the last word.

"I hope so," answered Vane mechanically, and not as much alarmed as he ought to have been. "O, by the way, where is Sharp? I want to see him about this."

"Yes, you'd better see him," said Dorman, who was counting his bills, all miser again. "You'll find him at home."

MR. Simon Sharp, the member from the old Whetstone State, was, it must be understood, the real head of the Great Subfluvial corporation, and also of that interior manifestation of it which we have called the Hen Persuader.

As Vane hurried toward this honorable's house, he met that eminent and venerated, but just now grievously slandered statesman, Mr. Greatheart. The two could not pass each other without a moment's discourse. By the way, there was a vast deal of mysterious, muttered conversation going on just now among Congressmen. They had a subject in common, a subject of terrifying interest to only too many of them, the subject of this approaching, unavoidable investigation. You could scarcely turn a corner without discovering a couple of broad-backed, thick-necked, and big-headed gentlemen leaning solemnly toward each other and engaged in such cautious, inaudible communion that it seemed as if they were speaking only through their staring eyes, or by means of some twitching of their noses. The number of these duos, the noiseless gravity with which they were conducted, the usually swollen configuration of the performers in them, and the stupefied astonishment which was depicted in their faces, all reminded one of those numerous solemn meetings of toads which may be seen after a shower.

Mr. Greatheart was not physically such a man as you might have expected from his heroic name. There was not a line about him, either in the way of muscle or expression, which could suggest descent from that stalwart knight who guided Christiana through the Dark Valley. He was short and squat in build, with a spacious, clean-shaved, shining face, huge red wattles of cheeks hanging down over his jaws, and a meek, non-combatant, semi-clerical mien. A bacchanalian cardinal, who should lately have turned Quaker, but lacked time to get the Burgundy out of his complexion, might wear a similar physiognomy. There was conscience in this visage, but there was also spiritual pride and animal propensity, and perhaps other evidences of a nature not yet made perfect. Good people who believed in him knew him as a man whose public career was famed for being spotless, and whose private life had been smirched here and there by innuendo.

Just now the Honorable Greatheart was evidently in low spirits, not to say in a bewildering funk. Recalling our batrachian simile, we might describe him as a toad who looked as if he had eaten too many ants and got the dyspepsia. In real truth he was ready to call on mushrooms to hide him, and on molehills to cover him. His condition was a sorry one, much sorrier than John Vane's. He had pocketed Hen Persuader stock, and then had publicly and positively denied the fact, either to save his own reputation from the charge of bribery, or to lighten the party ship over the breakers of the election. Now there was to be an investigation, and the ownership of this malodorous property would be traced to him, and he would be convicted of lying. Is it any wonder that under such circumstances a reputed saint should have somewhat the air of a reptile?

"Glad to see you, Vane," he murmured, shaking our member's hand fervently, for he was a cordial man when in adversity. "What do you judge to be the prospects about an investigation?"

"Sure to come on, I hear," answered John, who was much cheered by the results of his interviews with Ironman and Dorman, and remembered that he might yet sit in judgment on Greatheart.

"So I understand," sighed that stumbled worthy, his wattles drooping still lower and taking a yellowish tint. "Ah well! we may suffer severely for this error. I conceive now, Mr. Vane, that it was an error. Yes, it was a really terrible mistake," he went on conceding, for he was in that mood of confession which gripes unaccustomed misdoers under the threatenings of punishment. "A blunder is sometimes worse than a crime, — that is, worse in its consequences. And circumstances are such in Washington that the best-intentioned of us are occasionally beguiled into very sad blunders."

"In spite of everything that we can do," eagerly affirmed Vane, classing himself of course among the "best-intentioned."

"Very few men are really fit for Congress," pursued Mr. Greatheart, in a certain preaching tone which was natural to him, he having once been a clergyman. "I sometimes feel that I myself ought never to have come here. I had neither the pecuniary means nor the stoical character to grapple with the protean life of Washington. It is too full of exigencies and temptations for any human nature which is not quite extraordinary. The legislative system alone is enough to kill us. As long as these subsidy bills and relief bills are allowed, no man ought to run for Congress who is not a Crœsus or a Cato. A poor fellow *will* get into debt, and then the lobby offers to help him out, and it is very hard to refuse. The whole arrangement is terribly severe on men of small means."

"Just so," feelingly assented Vane, who heard his own decline and fall narrated, and was moved to compassion by the tale. "It's too bad on us. Either the whole system of special legislation ought to be done away with, or else we ought to be allowed a regular percentage on the appropriations we vote, and the thing made business-like."

"That — that is a bold idea," smiled Greatheart, apparently not disapproving it. "Are you thinking of proposing it?"

"O, no!" exclaimed John, drawing back bodily in the earnestness of his negation. "I suppose it would cost a fellow his re-election."

"I suppose it would, unless he represented a very staunch district," said Greatheart. "I don't know but one man who would dare advocate such a plan. I think — if you have no objection — that I'll mention it to General Boum."

And so these two penitents, who were ready to resume thievery as soon as they could get free from their crosses, bade each other a sad good morning and parted.

Next John found Mr. Sharp, and was received by him with razor-strop smoothness, as that well-oiled gentleman received everybody who could vote on his schemes.

"Do take a seat, Mr. Vane, — take a seat without ceremony," he begged, meanwhile softly handling his visitor by the arms, much as though they were glass ones. "Let me offer you this easy-chair. You honor me by accepting it. I thank you kindly."

Vane had an instinctive desire to look at the sleeves of his overcoat. It always seemed to him, after Mr. Sharp had fingered him, as if he must be greasy.

"I am exceedingly glad to see you here," continued the Whetstone representative, gazing as genially as he could at our member through his cold, vitreous eyes. "I had begun to fear that I was under such a cloud of misrepresentation and obloquy that my old friends would not come to call on me. This great enterprise, which I have had the honor to foster a little, according to my poor measure of financial ability, has been terribly abused and maligned. A national enterprise, too! a thing not only beneficial, but absolutely necessary to the country! The noblest scheme ever indorsed by the wisdom of Congress! What *do* people mean? What does the *press* mean? What is this investigation *for?* I am completely bewildered."

"It's giving the stock to Congressmen that has made the row," answered Vane, who judged that they might as well come to the point at once.

"O, *that* is it?" grinned Mr. Sharp, with an air of getting light in the midst of really discouraging darkness. "I am glad you have explained it to me. I should have expected it from a man of your clearness of vision. I thank you kindly. Well — as to that matter — why, that is simple. I put the stock where it would do the most good to a good thing."

"Just so," nodded Vane, meanwhile thinking what nonsense it was for Sharp to be talking gammon to *him*. "But you see — Well, never mind about that now; we may as well get to business. There is sure to be an investigation."

"Exactly," answered the Whetstone member, sloughing off his coating of "soft sawder," and coming out as hard and bright as a new silver dollar.

"And I have a smart chance of being put on the House committee," continued John.

Mr. Sharp opened the dark-lantern of his Puritanic visage, and let out a smile which contained all the guile of all the peddlers that ever sold wooden nutmegs.

"Mr. Vane," said he, "are your arrangements about that stock of yours completed to your entire satisfaction?"

"I have paid Dorman for it and got a receipt that will do me."

"Mr. Vane, do let me hand that money back," pursued Sharp, fumbling in his desk and producing a package of bills. "It was a trifling mark of private amity and sincere esteem. I never meant it should be paid for. Dorman is an able business man, but hasn't an idea beyond trading. I insist, Mr. Vane, on your taking back your money."

"Well — from that point of view — since you will have it so," smiled Dishonest John, pocketing the bills.

"Want any more of the stock?" inquired Sharp, with a cunning twinkle in his half-shut eyes, as if he saw a way to recover his thousand dollars.

"No!" answered Vane, not less promptly and positively than if he had been offered a ladleful of pitch from the infernal caldron.

"My dear sir, we are at your service," bowed the financier. "Anything that we can do for you, call on us. Of course you will have all our influence towards putting you on that committee. *Must* you go? So obliged for this call! Let me open the door for you. Thank you kindly."

23

THANKS to the labors of solemn Mr. Sharp and of worldly Mr. Ironman, our member soon had a fair prospect of getting on the investigating committee, supposing always that there should be such a nuisance.

But the nearer he came to this post of responsibility and honor, the more it looked to him as though it might turn out a whipping-post, at which he would stand with exposed shoulders and bleeding cuticle. If he as a judge should be able to close the court-room doors, and keep out not only spectators but also the witnesses in the case, all might go famously well, at least from the Satanic point of view. But if, while pretending to examine into the little games of others, the same kind of cards should be found up his own sleeves, he would be ruined beyond a hope of re-election. The sad state of a boy whose pockets are full of fire-crackers in a state of crackling and scorching ignition, would be but a feeble image of such a disaster. In these days he vacillated as rapidly and disagreeably as if he were astride some monstrous shuttlecock, or were being seesawed by all the giants of fairy-tale land. His pulpy pink face wore an air of abiding perplexity which rivalled that of his Dundrearyish friend,

Ironman. At times it seemed as if its large watery features would decompose entirely with irresolution, and come to resemble an image of strawberry ice which has been exposed to too high a temperature.

Meantime, the spectre of investigation advanced, and its pointing finger renewed his sense of guilt. The approach of punishment always enlightens a sinner marvellously as to the heinous nature of his sin. Even the Devil, when visited by the hand of sickness, perceived that he had led an evil life, and hungered to withdraw from a world of temptation and thirsted to take holy orders. Just so John Vane now discovered plainly once more that he had been pocketing bribes and swindling the public treasury, and that these were very wrong actions. If he had never truly had a conscience before, but had regulated his conduct by the consciences of others, he at last possessed one of his own. Indeed, it appeared to him a very large one because it was sore, precisely as a man's nose seems large to him while yet tender from a fisticuff. From one point of view, he was an honester John Vane than he had ever been, inasmuch as terror and remorse made him intelligently honest with himself.

Before he could decide to accept a position on the committee, he must be sure that Sharp & Co. would conceal his ownership of their stock, and he called on Dorman to obtain a positive promise to that effect. It is wonderful, by the way, how rogues in distress will trust each other's word, even when each knows by experience that the other is a confirmed liar.

"Look here, Darius, the more I stir up this business, the worse it looks to me," he groaned from the summit of a state of mind which almost raised him to the moral altitude of a penitent thief.

Dorman responded by groaning over his end of the burden, which naturally seemed to him much heavier than Vane's; each of these invalids, like the majority of commonplace sick people, wanted to talk of his own malady and symptoms. Still, there was a sort of fellow-feeling between them, such as even small-pox patients have for each other. Dorman no longer purposed financial vengeance upon Vane for getting his stock at par and paying no commission. Nor was Vane sensibly embittered against Dorman, although the latter had made a large fortune out of the Subfluvial, while he himself had only pocketed a beggarly thousand or two.

"It's the cursed unfairness of the thing that yerks me," the lobbyist complained. "Now isn't it too bad that the public should want to haul our job over the hottest kind of coals, when ever so many other jobs just like it ain't spoken of?"

We must remark here, what the reader has doubtless already noticed, that there was something disappointing in this creature's conversation. While his person and demeanor reminded one of the supernatural castaways of the lake of fire, his discourse was insignificantly human and even smacked of a very low down sort of humanity.

"And here I am in it, for almost nothing," sighed Vane, returning instinctively to his own case. "What sort of a story are you going to tell, Darius, if they put you on the stand?" he presently inquired.

"O, I would say anything that would do the most good," grimaced the lobbyist. "But Sharp means to let out a few facts; that is, if they crowd him. You see, Sharp unluckily has a character to nurse. I dare say, too, he thinks he can stop questions by showing that he means to answer them," added Dorman, who always imputed the lowest motives.

Thoroughly scared by this information, Vane resolved to keep off the committee. He went home in the dumps, wished he had never gone into politics, and meditated resigning his seat. Perhaps he would have taken this wholesome step, but he was moved first to consult Olympia about it, and she flatly refused to resign.

"I won't agree to it, — no, never!" she exclaimed, rustling in all her silks with indignation. "Why, I have just fairly got into the best society, and there are all the receptions to come, and the inauguration ball! and the winter is going to be *so* gay!"

"O — well," stared John, who had not thought to look at this side of the medal; "but we must stick to boarding, if we do stay," he capitulated on conditions. "I tell you the winter ain't going to be gay in Congress, and there won't be much money lying around loose, and we *must* skimp."

Before many days he found cause to pluck up his courage a little. He learned that Slowburgh considered him innocent of evil, meaning, of course, that half of Slowburgh which had voted for him. The committee of a certain association sent him an invitation to lecture before it, and promised that "the appearance of his honest face on their platform would be the signal of frantic applause." Furthermore, certain newspapers remarked that, although John Vane was suspected of owning Hen Persuader stock, he had at least not denied such ownership, and commented upon the fact as an unusual exhibition of uprightness and manliness — in a Congressman. These things revived his confidence so much that his mind was able to work. He saw his game clear before him; he must get in a "long suit" of frankness. There was a little trick, which, if skilfully and luckily played, would give him such a repute for veracity and for just intentions that all the caverns of the Great Subfluvial could not swallow it. What this happy thought was we shall learn presently.

Meantime the excitement of the men outside politics increased. That vast, industrious, decent American public, which wire-pullers usually regard as having no more intelligence or moral principle than one of the forces of nature, showed unmistakably that it possessed much political virtue and some political sense. The discovery that the so-called slanders against its favorites were, in all probability, verities, only made it more determined that those slanders should be investigated. The steady tempest of its righteous indignation scattered good seed through Congress, and produced on that upland of statesmanship a promising nubbin or two of conscience. An investigation was ordered, at first under hermetically sealed conditions, but the popular storm soon blew the doors open.

The rest we mainly know; the whole alien world of monarchies, empires, and despotisms knows it; the capacity of republicanism for honest government is everywhere being judged by it. In every civilized land on this planet, thoughtful souls are seeking to divine, by the light of these and other similar dolorous revelations, whether it is possible for a democracy to save itself from the corrupting tyranny of capital. Within our own borders sadder spirits are asking which is the most alluring spectacle, — a free America falling into squandering and bribery, or a monarchial Prussia ruled by economy and honesty.

We know how it fared with Christian and Faithful and Hopeful and Greatheart and other venerated statesmen who had turned more or less into the ways of Achan and Ananias. Anxious to clear themselves of an ugly charge, and trusting that the chief manipulator of the Hen Persuader would be willing to bear their sins in return for their services, they had flatly denied having taken any golden eggs out of his abstracting machine. But this disclaimer left Mr. Simon Sharp under the imputation of putting said eggs into his own pocket, and so plundering his partners in the enterprise of making the national hen lay on indefinitely. Being a man of exact arithmetical instincts, and of inveterate, ingrained business habits, he revolted from such an unfair allotment of the dividends of dishonor, and insisted that every one should take his own share and no more. To the astonishment of everybody, he told a story as straight and searching as a ploughman's furrow; and we will venture to say that no American was proud of the unexpected skeletons which it turned up. There was a time when every fair political reputation reminded us of the Arabian oil-jars, each one of which held a robber; when it seemed as if we should have to concede that our legislative temple was but a den of thieves, sadly given to lying. It was a new and perversely reversed and altogether bedevilled rendering of the *Pilgrim's Progress* into American politics; it was much as if Bunyan had at the last pitched *his* Christian and Hopeful into the little lurid hole which led from the gate of Zion to the pit. Nothing could well be more subverting and confounding and debilitating to the moral sense, unless it might be to see silver Demas and filthy Muckrake welcomed by the shining ones into the Holy City.

And something similar to this last marvel was not wanting.

24

WEATHER-COCK JOHN

carried out his plan for getting up a new and revised edition of his character as Honest John Vane.

He let Sharp and Ironman go on working for him, declaring that he was the most upright creature on this footstool, and recommending him as fit to investigate the very claims of saints to their crowns. But when his name was read as a member of the committee, he rose and requested to be excused from serving.

"My reason is simply this," he said, calmly turning his honest face and dignified abdomen towards every quarter of the house; "I own stock — to the amount of one thousand dollars — in the corporation in question. I will offer no explanations here and now as to my motives in taking it, because those motives will doubtless be demanded of me by the committee of investigation. I shall be happy to appear before it, but I cannot conscientiously be a member of it. I trust that the House, and you, Mr. Speaker, will excuse me."

The Honorable Sharp looked icicles from his armchair, and Dorman looked coals of fire from his rear corner. But as our member sat down there was a general murmur of perfunctory applause, and by next morning he was newspapered all over as "Honest John Vane."

Still, he was not out of danger. As the rain of fire and brimstone into the Congressional Sodom continued, and especially when the blazing flames of investigation began to light on his own combustible garments, he was in a state of mind to flee into the mountains and dwell in a cave. When he appeared before the committee, he did not look much like one of those just men whose mere presence can save a wicked city. Moreover, Sharp and Dorman testified against him to the full extent of their naughty knowledge. Nevertheless, Vane came out of his furnace without much of a singeing. He exhibited Dorman's receipt of payment for the stock, and triumphantly remarked that "the document spoke for itself." As for the thousand dollars which Sharp had refunded to him, he said that he had always regarded it as a loan, and stood ready to repay it. As for the singular profitableness of the investment, — well, he had expected it would bring him in something handsome; it was his habit as a business man to invest for a profit.

He tried to raise a smile here, turning his genial visage from one to another of the committee, with an almost pathetic effort at humor. But the sad synagogue of investigators did not smile back; it had been engaged that morning in digging graves for some of the fairest reputations in politics; for once a body of Congressional Yoricks could not appreciate a poor joke.

"What we mainly wish to know," hummed and hawed the worried chairman, "is whether you were aware, at the time of purchase, that the Hen Persuader was a branch of the Great Subfluvial corporation."

Weathercock John was in dire trouble; if he said "Yes," his character and career were ruined; if he said "No," he was a perjurer. It cost him many seconds of penal meditation to hit upon that happy dodge known as the *non mi ricordo*.

"Gentlemen, I will frankly confess that I did not inquire so closely as I perhaps should have done into that point," he answered, remembering distinctly that he had not inquired into it at all, but had been told all about it by Dorman. "I did, however, know that the two companies were acting under different and independent charters. It seemed fair to infer that investing in one was not the same thing as investing in the other."

It was done. Congressman Vane had found his own way out of his entanglements. The committee-men were ready to rise and salute his escape with benevolent cheers. How in the name of political human nature could they want to find guilty their brother lawgiver, brother worker in the party traces, and, perhaps, brother sinner in special legislation? They bowed him away from their operating table with a look which said plainly, We rejoice that we shall not be obliged to amputate your able and honored head, Mr. Vane.

Only a few people remarked on the shallowness of this show of innocence. Here was stock sold at par which was worth three hundred, which on the day after purchase paid a dividend of sixty per cent, and, only a few weeks later, forty more. How could a legislator and business man doubt that it was a swindle? How could he fail to divine that Mr. Sharp's Hen Persuader was but an adjunct of Mr. Sharp's Great Subfluvial?

But the public, — the great, soft-hearted American public, — that public which has compassion on every species of scoundrel, — which tries murderers under jury restrictions warranted to save four-fifths of them, — which cannot see one condemned to death without pleading with tears for his noxious life, — that forgiving, milk-and-water public was as mild in its judgment as the committee. It magnified our dishonorable member for not lying, and exalted his name for not committing perjury. What a pity, said this lamblike public which was so bent on getting itself fleeced to the skin, — what a pity that our other shepherds could not have used the shears with a steadier hand and avoided snipping off their own fingers! In contrast to these unlucky and somewhat ridiculous bunglers, what a straightforward, workmanlike, admirable creature was "Honest John Vane."

And so he escaped all exposure that could injure him in the eyes of a community of humanitarians, and all punishment that could hurt a man whose conscience lay solely in the opinions of others. Even the Subfluvial people did not follow him up vindictively; they admired him so much for his ability in sneaking that they could not hate him; moreover, they considered that he might still be useful. Not long after Vane's escape from the committee, he held with Dorman one of those friendly colloquies which rogues are capable of when it no longer pays to quarrel.

"What a horrid scrape Christian and Greatheart have got themselves into!" observed John, with cheerful self-complacency. "Why couldn't those fellows have told a straight story?"

"Half-honesty is cursed poor policy," smirked the lobbyist. "After all, those chaps are the cleanest-handed of the whole gang. They wanted to make an actual investment, — something that would show like a fair business transaction, — just to ease their consciences. The real sharpers took greenbacks and kept their names off paper. Do you suppose that the committee is raking up the Subfluvial to the bottom? Why, our very first move, the mere getting our charter through, cost us half a million. We have paid out hundreds of thousands to men against whom we haven't a particle of proof beyond our verbal statements."

"Exactly," nodded Vane, who had long since heard as much. "Well, do you mean to swear in these things?"

"Of course we don't," Dorman chuckled. "We know enough not to kill the goose that lays our golden eggs."

"So much the worse for the Greatheart lot," inferred Weathercock John. "They will have to go out, I suppose."

"Don't you believe it," scoffed the lobbyist. "I can tell you exactly how this thing is sure to come out. There will be a one-legged report, — somebody giving bribes, but none of the takers guilty of being bribed, — like a gambling case in which only one of the players is a gambler. Then, if the public excitement keeps up, a couple or so will be picked out as scapegoats, to bear off the sins of the congregation. This report will be so manifestly unfair that it can't help rousing opposition. As soon as it appears, a debate will be arranged. All the old war-horses will gallop up and down among charges, counter-charges, precedents, and points of law, raising such a dust that the public won't be able to see what is going on. When the dust clears away, it will be found that nobody is expelled. The two scapegoats will be almost expelled, but not quite. It will be like the pig going through the crooked hollow log and always coming out on his own side of the fence. Then the wire-pullers at home will take a hand in the job. All the convicted chaps will have receptions got up for them in their districts, and be whitewashed all over with resolutions expressing unshaken confidence. *You* won't have any reception, John. You are not far gone enough to need such vigorous treatment. Your case is lobby varioloid, instead of lobby small-pox."

Vane felt somewhat offended at this plain speaking, for it is a curious fact that he had not lost his self-esteem; but, looking at matters in his habitual profit-and-loss way, he decided that wrath would bring him in nothing.

"Take care of yourself, Dorman," he said, with a tranquil good nature which did him dishonor. "If I owned a million of your style of property, I shouldn't feel rich. There'll be suits against your inside corporation."

"I'm out of it," replied the lobbyist, flashes of cunning dancing about his sooty eyes, as sparks run over the back of a foul fireplace. "I have failed."

For the life of him, and notwithstanding the long-faced decorum which sham honesty requires, John Vane could not help laughing. The fact that a financier should declare himself bankrupt the moment he saw himself in danger of being called on to refund his swindlings, did not strike our self-taught legislator as a very disgusting exhibition of rascality, but as a very amusing bit of cleverness.

"But you're going to hang around here, I hope," he added, unwilling to lose a trickster who had been helpful, and might be so again.

"No, I am going *back*," said Dorman, in a tone which would have been significant of forebodings and horrors to any soul less carnal than a sparerib. His face, too, was strange; it had an unusually seared, cindered, and smoke-stained look; one would have said that the cuticle was drying up with inward heat. If that scorched envelope had cracked open, and the creature within had bounced forth in some different hide, or in a raw-head-and-bloody-bones state of nudity, there would have been no great cause of wonderment. But Congressman Vane saw nothing remarkable; he simply inquired, with calm, oleaginous interest, "Going back *where?*"

"Where I came from," grimaced Dorman, and disappeared abruptly, either by stepping briskly around a corner, or by slipping under a flagstone.

Not in the least disturbed by this singular circumstance, and, indeed, altogether failing to perceive anything noteworthy in it, Weathercock John marched on majestically to the Capitol, and commenced his day's work of statesmanship.

Well, there he is still, a lawgiver to this tax-burdened people, and *ex-officio* a director of its finances. As soon as he has recovered from his present slight scare, he will resume his labor (the only legislative labor which he knows much about) of enacting the national revenue into the safes of huge corporations and into the hats of individual mendicants, for the sake of a small percentage thereof to himself. Can nothing be done to stop him, or at least to shackle and limit him, in his damaging industry? Can we not wrest from him and from his brother knaves or dunces this fearfully abused privilege of voting the public money for other objects than the carrying on of the departments of the government? Can we not withdraw altogether from Congress the power of aiding corporations and schemers out of an income which is contributed by all for the equal benefit of all? Can we not provide, for instance, that, if a man has a claim for injuries to property against the United States, he shall prosecute that claim in the courts?

Such men as John Vane will inevitably find their way in numbers to the desks of the Capitol. Better and wiser men than he will be corrupted by a lobby which has thoroughly learned the easy trick of paying a hundred thousand out of every stolen million. Nothing in the future is more certain than that, if this huge "special legislation" machine for bribery is not broken up, our Congress will surely and quickly become, what some sad souls claim that it already is, a den of thieves.